Organic Livestock Farming

Principles, Practices and Profits

Edited by

D. Younie

SAC, Craibstone Estate, Bucksburn, Aberdeen AB21 9YA

and

J.M. Wilkinson

School of Biology, University of Leeds, Leeds LS2 9JT

Papers presented at conferences held at the Heriot-Watt University,
Edinburgh, and at the University of Reading,
9 and 10 February 2001.
Organised by David Younie and Malla Hovi.

SAC

University of Reading

sponsored by

 **The Royal Bank of Scotland plc**

 **FARMERSWEEKLY**

CHALCOMBE

D0675640

First published in Great Britain by
Chalcombe Publications
Painshall, Church Lane, Welton,
Lincoln, LN2 3LT.
United Kingdom

© Chalcombe Publications 2001

ISBN 0 948617 45 4

Printed in Great Britain by Ruddocks Colour Printers, Lincoln.

Contents

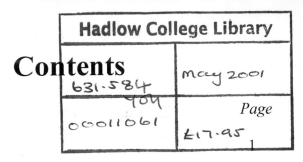

Foreword

DAVID YOUNIE

*Agronomy Department, SAC, Craibstone Estate, Bucksburn,
Aberdeen AB21 9YA*

This book is the proceedings of two major conferences for livestock farmers held in Edinburgh and Reading in early February 2001. It is a 'state of the art' guide focussing on the technical aspects of organic livestock production. Five recent developments combine to highlight the need for such a guide:

a) There has been a very rapid expansion recently in the number of farmers converting to organic livestock production. In many instances this has involved a rush to convert out of desperation because of very poor prices of conventional products, without a full understanding of either the organic standards themselves, or the basic principles which lie behind these standards. Farmers' need for information on organic livestock production has never been greater.

b) In England and Wales, the Ministry of Agriculture, Fisheries and Food (MAFF) Organic Farming Scheme opened again for applications on 1 January 2001, having been closed for a year, although the Scottish Executive Organic Aid Scheme has remained open for applications during this period.

c) The expansion in organic livestock farming has coincided with major changes to the organic livestock standards as a result of the implementation in August 2000, of the European Union (EU) Regulation 1804/1999. Farmers and certification bodies are faced with the challenge of coming to terms with the new rules.

d) Results and experience are coming through from organic livestock and grassland research funded by MAFF, the Scottish Executive Rural Affairs Department (SERAD) and the EU. Organic livestock farmers, whether long-converted, recently-converted, or just thinking about conversion, can now benefit from the results of this research.

e) Marketing has long been a weak link in the organic livestock sector but developments in recent years, particularly with cooperatives and other initiatives, have led to improved market infrastructure and better long-term prospects. For this reason, marketing is considered the most important topic and is therefore considered first.

The conferences, organised by the Scottish Agricultural College and University of Reading, focussed on 'Principles, Practicalities and Profits'. The programme covered everything from marketing, through principles and certification, to animal health strategies and grassland, and then focussed on organic dairy, beef, sheep, pigs and poultry enterprises in turn. An expert team of contributors was brought together, including commercial farmers, advisors and researchers, all with long experience of organic livestock production. Each contributor concentrated on the essential issues in their subject area, describing best current practice and highlighting problem areas where solutions still need to be found.

The outcome will be a better-informed, more efficient and more profitable organic livestock sector.

Chapter 1

The Marketing of Organic Milk: Opportunity and Challenge

S. BAGENAL
Organic Milk Suppliers Cooperative Ltd
Court Farm, Loxton, Near Axbridge, Somerset BS26 2XG

INTRODUCTION

The market for organic food in the UK has traditionally been dominated by fruit and vegetables. As recently as 1998, around 50% of total sales of organic food were made up of fruit and vegetables. In contrast, livestock produce has comprised a relatively small proportion of total sales. However, between 1994 and 1999 annual retail sales of organic milk and dairy produce increased dramatically (Table 1.1). In a three-month period during 1999, Sainsbury's liquid milk sales doubled.

Table 1.1   Retail sales of organic dairy products 1994-1999 (Mintel, 1999)

	Sales (£ million at 1994 prices)	Per cent of all organic sales
1994	6.1	5
1996	13.2	7
1998	32.5	9
1999 (estimate)	50.8	10

Clearly the supply increased during this period and, although there are several reasons for this expansion (including an increasing price differential between organic and conventional milk and the attraction of organic aid payments), part of the reason has undoubtedly been an improved market infrastructure for organic milk, in particular the establishment of a strong producer group - the Organic Milk Suppliers' Cooperative.

COOPERATION WITH PROCESSORS AND RETAILERS

The Organic Milk Suppliers Cooperative (OMSCo) was set up in 1994, by five founder producer-members who believed that a new way of marketing milk could be found. A meeting with Tim Mead from Yeo Valley had shown that the relationship between farmer and processor did not necessarily have to be negative or antagonistic. This discussion demonstrated that producers and processors could plan and work together to develop a new market, that processors could be appreciative of producers' problems and that in turn farmers as suppliers could thrive and expand in this environment.

Firm contracts between OMSCo and processors, based on fairness and mutual respect, were drawn up and prices fixed. Non-confrontational negotiations took place when increases in price were needed and ideas flowed on how to take the market forward. One of the objectives in this developmental process was for OMSCo and its members to feel connected to the market. It was agreed with three of the buyers that a bonus payment would be made to OMSCo at the end of each year that would represent a proportion of buyer profits. These funds were to be used to develop the Coop further, if necessary, or passed back to the members. Our producer members have benefited from these relationships and last year received bonuses of just over 0.3 pence per litre.

In 1999, OMSCo made a ground-breaking deal with a supermarket company, Sainsbury's. This contract, which gave a rolling five-year commitment on price and volume, was not made on the basis of OMSCo making demands because it controlled the majority of supply, but again was negotiated by mutual respect and agreement about what needed to be done to develop the market. Sainsbury's approach in negotiating this contract was atypical for a supermarket company, but has proved to be totally crucial because it has given a large number of dairy farmers the confidence to begin conversion to organic production. It is tempting to conclude that the spirit of the Sainsbury's deal came from the spirit of OMSCo's relationships with its processors and that this kind of spirit can inform a market.

This spirit of trust, cooperation and integrity is at the heart of organic farming. Anyone trading in organic products must remember this. The urban organic consumer wants to believe in organic food and wants to believe that organic farmers, processors and retailers trade ethically and honestly. These partners in the sector must not give their customers cause for disillusionment.

COOPERATION BETWEEN PRODUCERS

In practice, for OMSCo, this means viewing all our members as equals, recognising the unique position that each farmer plays in his community and the importance of giving him or her the chance to prosper. Thus it is OMSCo's aim that all members receive the same price regardless of size or distance from the buyer. The milk price for the past three years has been 29.5 pence per litre, net of transport.

Members are asked to produce milk to a minimum of 3.7% butterfat and 3.20% protein. In turn, the members play their part, for example by keeping transport costs as low as possible by installing larger bulk tanks to facilitate every-other-day collection.

OMSCo does not pay seasonality payments, believing them to be a blunt instrument which tends to cause supply to lurch from under- to over-supply. Many of our buyers believe that they should be working with the farmers and their cows, that they should be innovative enough to balance their own supplies within their integrated businesses, as organic farmers have the more difficult balancing act to undertake. It is believed that the organic dairy sector should be moving away from a manipulative, production-based system and returning to a more natural system whereby the farmer works **with** his natural resources (land type and breeds) and seasonal weather patterns. As farmers who actually work the land and milk the cows, we should have a say in what we believe to be right. The current milk selling relationship between processor and producer is a sterile one, characterised by its price penalties and mistrust. There is a chance now to create improved relationships and a more balanced industry.

Just as there are no seasonality payments, the OMSCo milk price does not vary with bulk tank somatic cell count (SCC), provided it remains below the legal limit of 400,000. The critical question is whether a SCC of up to 400,000 has any affect on the making or keeping quality of a dairy product? Since the response from processors was that it does not affect product quality, the question then becomes one of what is best for the welfare of the cow. There is evidence to suggest that striving for very low SCC levels reduces immunity and increases the susceptibility of individual cows to outbreaks of severe mastitis.

OMSCo was the first group to offer financial support for farmers who wanted to convert to organic farming – plus free advisory support using the Elm Farm Organic Advisory Service. Unfortunately this financial support had to be withdrawn when the uptake became too much of a burden on the Coop. However, we believe that the best form of support or insurance, besides maintaining a stable market, was to offer the best advice and to make sure that farmers understood and performed to the highest possible standards of organic management. In 1999 OMSCo set up its own advisory structure, including a mentoring system - utilising the expertise of its own experienced farmer members who are paid for providing this assistance.

As organic farmers, we are our neighbours' keepers. One breach of the organic standards and the consequent media attention may disgrace the organic sector and destroy the trust and respect that has been gained and which many consumers are clearly searching for. It is important also for organic farmers not to be complacent, but instead to challenge themselves constantly to improve further the health and welfare of organic livestock and to minimise potential environmental impacts.

The success of OMSCo is heartening. Farmers from all over the UK share its vision. OMSCo Wales and OMSCo Scotland have now been established and their directors, whilst members of the main OMSCo board, dictate their own aspirations – such as making more of their respective national identities.

OMSCo has been very happy to co-operate with other milk groups in selling their organic milk, via the OMSCo long-term contracts. An excellent example of this is the current agreement being negotiated with Scottish Milk, with whom we share the same ideals of integrity and co-operation.

FUTURE POTENTIAL

Long term contracts such as those OMSCo is putting in place will provide a framework for the organic milk sector for years to come. After many months of consultation we have developed a formal pricing structure and set out negotiating procedures with processors. This structure will cushion the effect of any short-term upward or downward movement on price. The fact that large companies will sign up to this shows how far the industry has moved on co-operative thinking.

The stability of price that has been enjoyed so far has been the basis for the very satisfactory expansion that the organic dairy sector has seen in recent years. A boom and bust approach - uncontrolled expansion and a consequent rapid fall in organic milk price - will drive organic farmers out of business or back to conventional farming. The country will lose the benefits that organic dairy farming can offer.

Although 25% of milk in some outlets in North London is organic, organic milk production still represents less than one percent of UK production overall. The target of Sainsbury's and some other upmarket supermarkets is for 15% of their overall liquid milk sales to be organic by the year 2005. This will represent an average throughout the UK of about 5% or 350 million litres of all sales of dairy produce. This is a relatively modest proportion of the total liquid milk pool of 7 billion litres, and represents a production level equivalent to only 350 farmers each with a quota of one million-litres.

Caution is needed when we look at the potential size of the market in the next few years. Some supermarket representatives believe that expansion in the organic market has a very long way to go before a sales plateau is reached. They foresee a time in, say 15 years, when the majority of milk sold is organic and non-organic milk will become the economy range. What is clear now is that, with the advent of Wall-Mart, supermarkets will be looking to differentiate themselves in the struggle to maintain market share: they know that only one company will ever be the cheapest.

Thus the opportunity (and the necessity) for organic farmers is to stick together, to co-operate and plan ahead with our partners in the dairy industry and in the retail sector. This should include international co-operation. A vital first is the alliance that OMSCo has set up with organic farmer groups across Europe. Our first meeting in Denmark in January 2001 marked the beginning of co-operation and understanding of their trends and markets.

REFERENCE

Mintel (1999) *Organic Food and Drink*. Report by Mintel International Group Limited, November 1999.

Chapter 2

Marketing Organic Meat

M. R. CAMERON
farmgate.co.uk Ltd, Sovereign House, Sovereign Way, Tonbridge, Kent, TN9 1RW.

INTRODUCTION

This paper is intended neither as a statistical compendium relating to the organic meat market nor as an extensive critical appraisal of existing organic meat marketing chains. The purpose is to make the reader aware of the general trends in the market and the merits and downfalls of following different marketing routes. Any producer, whether on a long established organic unit or simply considering conversion, must continually evaluate the market for their stock and if necessary adapt their production system accordingly.

Environmental and ethical concerns remain high on the list of goals for the successful organic farmer but the reality is that producing the right product and marketing it efficiently will give the best chance of long term economic sustainability.

WHAT IS THE MARKET?

The market for organic meat is complex and difficult to quantify. In recent years market value for UK produced organic meat has shown annual growth rates nearing 100% (Soil Association, 1999). It is widely acknowledged that demand for organic meat continues to outstrip supply. As such, it is extremely difficult to quantify the true level of consumer demand.

The market for all types of organic food has shown great growth in the last 10 years but still remains a minority sector of the food market as a whole. Undoubtedly, the move by multiple retailers to increase available lines of organic food has helped the market grow, albeit fuelled by strong consumer demand.

While UK consumption of organic fruit and vegetables is reliant on imports for in excess of 80% of market share, home produced organic meat still comprised 95% of consumption in 1999 (Soil Association 1999). The market for organic meat remained small at a value of around £10m compared with a total value for UK production of £77m (Soil Association 1999). Increased overall demand for organic food has contributed to the growth of the market for organic meat, but increasing consumer awareness of animal welfare issues and lack of confidence following the peak of the BSE crisis in 1996 may well have done more to fuel consumer demand. In line with consumption of all organic foods, the UK continues to have low *per capita* consumption of organic meat when compared with other European countries (Mintel, 1997; Soil Association, 1999).

Such convincing market statistics coupled with improved rates of support payments are almost certainly responsible for the rapid increase in numbers of organic livestock producers in recent years. Sadly, unsustainable economic returns under conventional production regimes have led to unprecedented rates of conversion of marginal livestock units, with restricted growth rates occurring in England and Wales only when budgetary constraints forced the closure of the Organic Farming Scheme. Indeed in Scotland where such limiting factors did not occur, numbers of upland and hill farms converting to organic production between 1997 and 2000 showed near exponential growth.

Although this influx of new entrants to organic farming goes some way to fulfilling the demand for organic meat, it has not been without problems. Many hill units cannot finish stock and are reliant on lowground units purchasing store animals to finish on better ground. Unfortunately the scattered geographic spread of producers and the imbalance of store producers and finishers means that maintaining the organic status of stock has been difficult in the absence of structured and co-ordinated marketing channels. Improved marketing procedures will help, but a large part of the problem lies with the primary producer. Organic livestock production is distinct from conventional production systems in that the time lag from start of conversion to production of organic stock will always be at least 2 years. This period should provide sufficient time to plan marketing and indeed many producers use the time sensibly and do just that. However those involved in providing marketing services can provide many examples of producers making contact only weeks or even days before organic stock is ready for sale. Indeed a recent survey of Scottish producers (Espirito Santo, 2000) showed that almost 50% of producers in conversion or in organic production had made no arrangements for marketing produce or stock. It is hard to think of any other industry where such a major decision concerning production method would take place without some form of market consultation.

WHAT IS MARKETING?

For the purposes of this paper, we will concentrate on 'physical' marketing. That is the process by which meat gets from the farm to plate. Those with a particular interest in more in-depth marketing issues such as market demographics and brand perception issues are referred to the comprehensive reports of Mintel (1995, 1997, 1999).

As with conventional stock, a number of options are available to organic producers. Limitations do exist, with licensed abattoirs being notably absent from some major production areas, particularly facilities equipped to deal with pigs and poultry. Organic standards also prohibit some methods of marketing such as the live auction of prime stock, though this may not necessarily be economically disadvantageous.

There are four main marketing methods:

1. Producer Groups
2. Direct Consumer Sales
3. Direct Deadweight Sales
4. Auctions

The choice of marketing method will be determined by many factors including location of production relative to market opportunities and the type of stock produced. The potential for each method should ideally be assessed before conversion, but the established organic unit must also be aware of changing markets and new opportunities offered.

1.   Producer Groups

Farmer-controlled businesses (FCBs) have developed more quickly in continental Europe than in the UK, with the turnover of FCBs in the UK being equivalent to 43% of agricultural output compared with a range of 117% to 259% for Germany, France, Netherlands, Denmark, Ireland and Sweden. Livestock marketing through FCBs in the UK accounts for market share of only 17%, 13% and 34% for cattle, sheep and pigs respectively (NFU, 1999).

Anecdotal evidence suggests that producer groups account for significantly more marketing effort of organic livestock. National organic marketing co-operatives have long been in place for Scotland, Northern Ireland and England and Wales. More recently, regional initiatives have emerged in many areas where clusters of conversion to organic production have become evident.

In the mid to late 1990s co-operatives were instrumental in the evolution of the organic meat market to its current form. Without co-operatives, abattoirs could not have been persuaded to become licensed. It was also the energy and enthusiasm of producer groups which encouraged many units to begin conversion to organic production. Most importantly, it was the hard work in co-ordination of supply that convinced multiple retailers that they could work with groups of farmers to give consumers continuity and quality and thus provide a volume market for organic meat.

The concept and aims of a producer marketing group remain largely unchanged today:

- To allow producers to communicate directly with the market.
- To prevent fragmentation of the market.
- To maintain some control of pricing.
- To allow greater vertical integration within the market.

15

- Pooling produce to allow access to high volume markets.
- Co-ordination of supply to even out major peaks and troughs.

Successful organic marketing groups have embraced all of the above points. Perhaps the most important aspect of any group is to allow communication with the market. This is where organic groups have chosen not to follow the lead of many conventional marketing groups and deal only with processors or abattoirs. The fact that a producer group can make contact directly with the end market, large or small, provides great value to its members. The nearer the producer becomes to the consumer, the more likely that, given adequate communication, both parties can be satisfied with the transaction in all aspects including quality of produce, price, and time of delivery. The level of feedback to the producer allows the evolution of production systems that is necessary for any sector of primary food production to remain successful.

Although smaller niche market opportunities remain important for organic meat, volume will become the mainstay of any producer group. Inevitably, this means a move towards dealing with multiple retail outlets and their primary processors. In the past many producer groups have had experience of these markets, but on the whole the trend has been a failure to recognise the quality of information required to service the multiples effectively. The extremely high demand for organic meat in many cases has been the only reason that retailers retained interest.

It is essential that a strategy for gathering and disseminating information on medium term stock availability is established. It is clear that it is fruitless for individual groups to carry out this task. Even if all are accurate, price erosion and market fragmentation are likely if effective lines of communication are not established between groups. There is a need for regional groups to liase closely with other groups at all times. It is not suggested that lucrative small or local markets be relinquished, but failure to make co-ordinated efforts when dealing with high volume outlets could quickly lead to pricing problems which are so bitterly apparent in the conventional livestock sector.

Store animal trading is an area of great potential for trade within and between producer groups. Many areas of the UK simply do not have enough ground to finish stock. Any communications which can take place to facilitate trade between store producers and finishers will be beneficial to both parties. Co-ordination of stock availability figures will aid pricing structures and logistics of trading between different regions.

2. Direct Consumer Sales

Direct consumer sales will not suit every producer or system. The personality of the individual producer and time and facilities available are immediate limiting factors. Although often best employed by smaller scale production units, it is possible for direct sales to be profitable on larger units when used in conjunction with other marketing methods.

Several points must be considered with any direct sales enterprise:

- Capital cost of buildings and equipment.
- Availability / training of suitable staff.
- Availability of suitable licensed processing facilities.

- Wastage – it may be difficult to sell cheaper cuts. 'Any fool can sell steaks but what about the rest…'.
- Proximity to market and competition.

a)   *Farm shops and delivery schemes*

The number of farm shops has increased greatly in recent years. Typically successful ventures tend to be close to major towns situated on a main road. Quite often it may be necessary to purchase produce from off-farm sources to sell alongside home-produced meat e.g. fruit, vegetables. It may even be difficult to maintain an adequate home-produced product range all year round at all. Trade may often be heavily weighted towards weekends so demand on staff will peak heavily. Until patterns of trade become established over time it may be very difficult to ascertain day-to-day demand.

Although doorstep delivery has been long associated with fruit and vegetable box schemes, many producers have found that it offers a convenient way to avoid the problems associated with predicting demand and associated wastage when selling meat from a farm shop. Orders for meat are taken in advance, usually for larger amounts e.g. half or whole lamb, half pig, 25-kg beef pack, 6 chickens. This allows production and slaughter to become better planned and wastage to be minimised. Produce is delivered fresh, perhaps vacuum packed, to be frozen by the customer. This route allows less capital expenditure on premises and, depending on timing, perhaps allows for refrigerated transport to be hired rather than purchased. The only downfall may be that it is usually necessary to price produce at time of order which may be disappointing if the market value increases significantly in the meantime.

b) Mail order service

It is difficult to pick up any specialist food magazine or look at internet food directories without stumbling across an organic meat mail order company. This type of business may fit alongside a farm shop enterprise very well. Major issues to be considered are:

- Cost of advertising – print or web site
- Predicting demand is perhaps more difficult than with a farm shop
- Cost of suitable packaging materials
- Suitable delivery/courier service – reliability and cost
- Continuity of supply – are supplies available from other producers at problem times of year?

c) Farmers markets

Farmers markets have increased in popularity and are now present in most regions of the UK. Experience to date in many markets has been that many stallholders have sold out within an hour of two of opening. The points raised above are equally applicable to farmers markets with one additional *caveat* – what happens when you turn up with ten lambs butchered to sell and find ten other organic lamb producers are stallholders…?

3. Direct Deadweight Sales

Although most abattoirs are currently choosing to source organic stock via producer groups, this is likely to change as availability increases. It may be possible for larger producers to negotiate deals directly with a processor which are equivalent to or better than those offered by producer groups.

There are, however, obvious risks associated with relying on one outlet only. This type of marketing is largely confined to organic poultry and pigs at present, where long-term contracts are offered. Direct sales of beef and sheep are often subject to wildly fluctuating price schedules.

4. Auctions

It is extremely unlikely that primestock auction sales will ever fall within the bounds of UK organic standards. Although UKROFS standards do not specifically preclude the sale of livestock by auction, the year 2000 marked the first sales of organic stock with the approval of the Soil Association. It is anticipated that these sales of store stock will increase in years to follow.

Problems in getting a critical mass of animals entered for a sale, and to persuade a critical mass of buyers to attend, will emerge if sales are not conducted in a co-ordinated manner. Involvement of other marketing bodies such as producer groups working in conjunction with auctioneers should ensure that emphasis can be placed on a few large sales rather than many small ones.

In future the re-emergence of electronic auctions may be of special interest to organic producers. They offer the opportunity to offer stock to buyers over a wider geographic area and the concept fits well with some of the issues that have proved a sticking point in offering organic stock for sale at auction to date by:

- Preventing stock of different health status being mixed.

- Avoiding unnecessary travel to a selling point - stock can travel directly from seller to buyer.

5. Specification and Pricing

Specification of required quality for organic stock has always been an issue. Two camps emerge – those who believe that organic production should meet the same criteria as conventional livestock and those who believe that organic should mean an exclusive use of traditional breeds and more emphasis on meat quality. Both sides have valid points to make. In many cases, traditional breeds and crosses are more suited to organic production systems. However the use of breeds which produce an unsaleable or undesirable carcass is clearly unacceptable. When producing for specialist niche markets such as small butchers, it may be acceptable to have increased levels of fat cover, but the emphasis from volume markets is still towards a more conventional specification. Most multiple retailers are mindful that the nature of organic production means that controlling fat cover and weight may be more difficult and have in the main relaxed penalties associated with excess fat, lightweight and overweight animals.

The recent surge of hill producers undergoing conversion has led to an abundance of light lambs being available on the market. Conventionally, these lambs (10 to 14 kg carcass weight) are more suited to export markets. Work to date has shown that continental markets are reluctant to embrace organic lamb, though some producer groups have identified limited opportunities. Lamb is already viewed as a 'natural' product and the introduction of organic lines may undermine the value of this image. Urgent work is required to investigate markets for these lightweight lambs and other out of

21

specification carcasses. Organic convenience foods, baby foods and pet foods can all utilise poorer carcasses but to date, a lack of co-ordination to achieve critical volumes of meat becoming available has prevented these markets from being fully exploited.

Pricing of organic livestock has been and will continue to be a thorny issue. Much has been made in the farming press of the levels of organic premia available for stock. While it is acknowledged by all involved in the organic food industry that price differentials must be made over conventional prices, Robertson (personal communication, 2000) summed up the associated problems: "...a premium on a base price that is totally uneconomic is unlikely to end up with a viable business. Secondly, discussions about premia always give the impression to would-be buyers that there is some fat to be trimmed out of the system and needless to say the largest knife is always wielded at those with the least bargaining power - the primary producer.'

Any price negotiations in future must centre on the cost of production and not around percentage premiums over uneconomic conventional prices. This has caused a stir with many purchasers of organic stock who have strong business interests in the conventional sector. There must however be a realisation that economic sustainability is the only way which producers can continue to produce under organic production methods. Many producers have voiced the concern that while it is a testing process converting to organic production, it is very easy to revert to conventional production methods if viable prices are not achieved.

BEYOND 2001 – CONCLUSIONS

As the number of organic producers in the UK increases along with foreign competition, it becomes more important for producers to participate in co-ordinated marketing of livestock of the best quality possible. Complacency towards issues of quality may well stunt market growth or encourage import substitution. UK producers must improve the quality of stock offered and demonstrate the integrity of standards to the consumer. Failure to address market demand will lead to production of unsaleable product and uneconomic organic production systems. Failure to co-ordinate marketing schemes for finished and store stock may lead to organic stock being sold on the conventional market at reduced prices in the short term, creating a fragmented market where price erosion is inevitable.

Many producers have converted to organic production because they have had vision to see ahead of the economic problems that conventional production held. All organic producers must maintain a forward vision and efficient communication with the marketplace to ensure that marketing channels are optimised for their individual business giving the best possible chance of future economic success.

ACKNOWLEDEMENT

I am grateful to Mr Nigel Elgar, Cannon, Llanerfyl, Welshpool, Powys, SY21 0JJ, for helpful discussions in the early stages of the preparation of this paper.

REFERENCES

Espirito Santo, J.I. (2000). *Investigate Appropriate Extension Provision for the Organic Sector in Scotland.* MSc Thesis, Aberdeen University.

Mintel (1995). *Vegetarian and Organic Foods.* Mintel Report, October 1995.

Mintel (1997). *Organic and Ethical Foods.* Mintel Report, November 1997.

Mintel (1999). *Organic Food and Drink.* Mintel Report, November 1999.

NFU (1999). *Farming Economy 1999* – Routes to Prosperity for UK Agriculture.

Soil Association (1999). *The Organic Food and Farming Report 1999.* Soil Association, Bristol.

Chapter 3

Principles of Organic Livestock Production

P. STOCKER
Soil Association, Bristol House, 40-56 Victoria Street, Bristol BS1 6BY

GENERAL PRINCIPLES

Organic farming is protected by EU Regulation (CEC, 1991, 1999) and is well defined through the organic standards (e.g. IFOAM, 1999; UKROFS, 2000; Soil Association, 2000). Just as importantly, the system is underpinned by a range of principles which have been defined for over 50 years, which is longer than either the organic standards or the legal definition.

The general principles of organic farming, as in IFOAM, UKROFS and Soil Association Standards are as follows:

- Co-exist with rather than dominate natural systems.
- Sustain or build soil fertility.
- Minimise pollution and damage to the environment.
- Minimise the use of non-renewable resources.
- Ensure the ethical treatment of animals.
- Protect and enhance the farm environment with particular regard to conservation and wildlife.
- Consider the wider social and ecological impact of agricultural systems.

- Maintain or develop valuable existing landscape features and adequate habitats for wildlife with particular regard to endangered species.

The market for organic food is largely founded upon these principles. Indeed there is a real danger that if we lose sight of them we may also lose the consumer support which the organic sector enjoys.

It is important to remember the holistic and interconnected nature of organic farming and the above principles. For example ruminant livestock are essential to utilise herbage legumes such as clover. This is the main generator of nitrogen (N) in organic systems, building up soil fertility which is in turn utilised later by arable crops, via the process of soil N mineralisation. In addition, livestock enhance biological efficiency in the farming system by utilising crop outgrades and wastes. Of course, through the production of manure, livestock also contribute to enhanced soil structure and fertility, and hence with arable crop production. The diversity of crops and livestock, which is a common feature of organic systems, enhances landscapes and habitats. Given good research and technical advances, and policy and market support, organic farming has the potential to appeal to a wide range of groups within society including farmers, environmentalists, conservationists, animal welfare organisations, health organisations, and those interested in improved social structures.

ORGANIC LIVESTOCK PRINCIPLES

As far as livestock production specifically is concerned, a recent report by the Food Ethics Council (Food Ethics Council,

2000) on the future of livestock production, considers "Two possible alternative scenarios: A high-tech approach to animal production (entailing the use of multiple ovulation,/embryo transfer, genetic modification and cloning), and a holistic approach, which is exemplified by organic farming." The council's analysis suggests that: "Although the high tech approach may prove effective in producing low cost products for the mass market, it is likely to entail major costs in terms of animal welfare, adverse effects on the environment and erosion of social and economic sustainability. Hence in the long run, organic farming could produce food more economically." Organic farming is only likely to do this if we do not lose sight of the well-founded principles listed above.

Farmers, both organic or conventional, can take two different approaches to crop and livestock husbandry decisions: a) the anticipatory or preventative approach involves designing the system to prevent problems arising in the first place; b) the reactive or fire brigade approach involves reacting to or controlling a problem after it has occurred. Clearly, organic farmers place most emphasis on the anticipatory approach, ensuring that problems such as animal disease are minimised. Some of the general principles of the EU Organic Livestock Regulation (CEC, 1999) are listed below to illustrate the approach which is taken in organic livestock production.

Origin of the animals

In the choice of breeds or strains, account must be taken of the capacity of the animals to adapt to local conditions; their vitality, and their resistance to disease. In addition, breeds or strains of animals should be selected to avoid specific diseases or health problems associated with some breeds or strains. Preference is to be given to indigenous breeds or strains.

Feed

Feed is intended to ensure high quality rather than maximal production, while meeting the nutritional requirements of the livestock at various stages of their development.

Disease prevention

Disease prevention in organic livestock production shall be based on the following principles:

a)   The selection of appropriate breeds and strains of animals.

b)   The application of husbandry techniques appropriate to the requirements of each species, encouraging strong resistance to disease and the prevention of infections.

c)   The use of high quality feed, together with regular exercise and access to pasturage, having the effect of encouraging the natural immunological defence of the animal.

d)   Ensuring an appropriate density of livestock, thus avoiding overstocking and any resulting animal health problems.

Livestock housing

Housing for livestock must meet their biological and behavioural needs as regards freedom of movement and comfort. The livestock must have easy access to feeding and watering. Insulation, heating and ventilation of the building must ensure that air circulation, dust level, temperature, relative air humidity and gas concentration, are kept within limits which are not harmful to the animals. The building must permit plentiful natural ventilation and light to enter.

Thus, instead of designing the system (in terms of breed choice, feeding, housing, etc) to push animals to perform as fast as possible, organic livestock production puts the animal's physiological, health, and behavioural needs first. Moderate performance levels are accepted as the price to pay for having contented animals, with minimal health problems.

FUTURE DEVELOPMENTS

It is relevant to discuss the current rapid expansion in organic farming and its relationship with the principles of organic production. There is no doubt that the overall picture is positive. The market is buoyant in most sectors, growth in UK production is rising at an average of 40% per year, and there are signs of increasing policy support. However this growth and expansion brings distinct pressures on the organic standards, including:

- Much of the growth in interest from conventional farmers converting to organic farming is financially driven. Many of these farmers, when they initially become interested, simply want easy access to a profitable market. In fairness, after conversion these farmers often become convinced of the intrinsic value of organic farming.
- A number of the supermarket chains, who collectively handle in the region of 70% of organic livestock products, are intent on driving the cost of organic food

down to a minimum, inevitably putting price pressure on producers and encouraging the cutting of corners in the organic standards.

- Further retailer pressure on UK producers comes from the ability of the multiple retailers to import organic livestock products, sometimes produced to lower standards than in the UK, and often supported by the ongoing maintenance payments to organic farmers in most other EU countries.
- Inappropriate technical advances that may provide short term solutions to immediate problems but will not address the situation in the longer term.
- In a desire by some retailers and conventional farmers to increase supply and make organic farming a mainstream option, there is pressure to relax standards in order to make the system suitable for all. This is symptomatic of the situation in other quality assurance systems, which have been established from a producer perspective, largely with the aim of maintaining producer prices. In contrast, the very strong brand image of organic produce has arisen because organic farming is a quality assurance system which has been developed more from a consumer perspective than from a producer perspective.

Regularly during discussions on standards development, and often during every day discussions on the farm, it is useful to have the principles of organic farming to fall back on in order to aid decision- making. Almost without fail, when a decision is difficult to make, the principles can be relied upon to provide the direction for the answer. The rapidly expanding organic movement will do itself a disservice to ignore them.

REFERENCES

CEC (1991). *Council Regulation No 2092/91 on organic production.* Official Journal of the European Communities, L198, 1-15.

CEC (1999) *Council Regulation No 1804/1999 supplementing Regulation No 2092/91 on organic production.* Official Journal of the European Communities, 42, L222, 1-28.

Food Ethics Council (2000) *Farming Animals for Food: Towards a Moral Menu.*3rd Report published in 2000 by Food Ethics Council, The Independent Council for Ethical Standards in Food and Agriculture

IFOAM, (1999) *Basic Standards of Organic Agriculture.* International Federation of Organic Agriculture Movements, Tholey-Theley, Germany

Soil Association (2000) *Soil Association Livestock Standards, incorporating Regulation 1804/1999.* Soil Association, Bristol.

UKROFS (2000). *UKROFS Standards for Organic Food Production. Standards for Organic Livestock and Organic Livestock Products.* United Kingdom Register of Organic Food Standards, London, August 2000.

Chapter 4

Certification of Organic Livestock Production

R. J. UNWIN
Farming and Rural Conservation Agency, UK Ministry of Agriculture, Fisheries and Food, Nobel House, 17 Smith Square, London, SW1P 3JR

INTRODUCTION

Unlike other market branding and assurance schemes, organic production is a legally defined system of food supply. The controls apply throughout the production, processing and supply chain. They also cover the importation and sale of organic products from anywhere in the world. Only food that has been subject to these controls may be labelled and sold as organic or under any other term that may be construed as implying organic status. Uniform crop and crop-processing standards have been in force throughout the European Union since 1991 (EU regulation 2092/91, CEC, 1991). Until 24 August 2000, when EU Regulation 1804/1999 was implemented (CEC, 1999), there were no common standards governing livestock production and each member state was free to set national standards.

This paper outlines the systems in place in the United Kingdom and the rest of the European Union to implement these controls

It will briefly consider some of the principles of the new livestock standards in order to highlight where standards may differ between individual member states of the European Union.

THE UK INSPECTION SYSTEM

The Board of UKROFS (The United Kingdom Register of Organic Food Standards) is the Certifying Authority for the UK. It is a Non Departmental Public Body undertaking these duties on behalf of the Minister of Agriculture in England and his equivalents in the other parts of the UK. UKROFS recognises seven Approved Sector Bodies to operate certification schemes for livestock farmers in the UK. Their schemes have been accepted as meeting not only the technical aspects of the standards (UKROFS, 2000) but that their procedures are compliant with the appropriate European Standard for accreditation bodies (EN 45011, CEC, 1989). Of the seven, two (Irish Organic Farmers and Growers Association and The Organic Trust) are based in the Republic of Ireland and as far as the UK is concerned, currently only operate in Northern Ireland.

The other bodies are the Biodynamic Agricultural Association, the Organic Food Federation, Organic Farmers and Growers Limited, Soil Association Certification Limited and Scottish Organic Producers Association. Additionally UKROFS currently offers direct certification and a small number of operators are certified under this scheme.

Generally, at the farm level the certification process involves the following procedure:

- The farmer decides which Sector Body to register with.
- He/she obtains a copy of the standards and an application form from the Sector Body.
- He/she completes and returns the form, together with the necessary fee. The Sector Body carries out an inspection. The farmer may start organic management before or after the inspection.
- The Inspector submits a report to the Certification Committee of the Sector Body.
- The farmer is informed by the Sector Body as to the success of his/her application. The two-year conversion period starts according to the date entered on the register of the sector body.
- The farmers must have his/her license renewed each year. An annual fee is payable.

UKROFS approval of the Sector Bodies is subject to ongoing monitoring of their performance. Not only does every symbol holder have to submit to at least one inspection per year from their Sector Body but also they may be subject to additional checks either announced or unannounced from their own Sector Body or by UKROFS inspectors. These latter checks by UKROFS are termed "audit inspections" and are currently undertaken on approximately 5% of all registered holdings. They are intended primarily to check the work of the inspectors and of the Sector Body, but serve also as an added check on the performance of the operatives.

The actions taken by the Sector Bodies as a result of their inspections are monitored to ensure that decisions are consistent with organic standards, fair to individuals and consistent between Sector Bodies. Symbol holders have a right of independent appeal against decisions of their Sector Bodies, as do the Sector Bodies themselves against decisions of UKROFS. The ultimate sanction of UKROFS is to remove the accreditation of a Sector Body. This might arise in response to persistent failure to meet its obligations. If this happened any symbol holders registered with the body concerned would have to register with another Sector Body if they wished to continue in organic production.

All inspectors have to be approved by UKROFS. This is now done by interview after an appropriate period of training. Inspectors also have a right of appeal if their performance is subsequently considered by UKROFS to be such as to warrant withdrawing their accreditation. From time to time UKROFS organises meetings between inspectors from different sector bodies to help maintain consistency of interpretation. The role of UKROFS is to ensure that all Sector Bodies apply at least the agreed UKROFS national standards, which have to be consistent with the European Regulation. It does not set out to ensure that a Sector Body is applying any standards they may have adopted, which are more restrictive than the agreed national rules.

CONTROLS IN OTHER EU COUNTRIES

The number of Sector Bodies in other countries varies from one in The Netherlands and in Portugal to over 20 in Germany where the Federal Lander system has lead to a proliferation of Bodies. It is understood that only the UK operates the dual system of accreditation and checking afforded by the UKROFS surveillance system described above. That said all Sector Bodies are required to follow at least the minimum European Standard and will be subject to control from the Member State concerned.

This equivalence means that once produce is certified anywhere in the EU by a recognised body it has free movement and can be labelled and sold as organic in any Member State. Therefore the UK cannot deny entry or sale to any such certified material even if, as described below for livestock, different standards are in force in different Member States.

IMPORTS FROM OUTSIDE THE EU

Any imports to the EU which are to be sold as organic, or which will form part of processed organic foods, must have been produced to equivalent standards to those pertaining in Member States. This can be demonstrated in two ways. Firstly, a limited number of third countries have applied to the European Commission to have their national system of accreditation recognised by the EU and when this has been done certified production has the same status as that approved by Sector Bodies within the EU. Alternatively, where no approval at EC level has been given, the importer has to seek approval from the competent National Authority e.g. UKROFS in the UK, that an equivalent system of certification has been applied to the product in question. Such certification may be by an organisation in the country concerned, or by an inspector from elsewhere, often from recognised sector bodies within the EU. In all cases the would-be importer has to provide UKROFS with full details of the standards and inspection measures applied, so that an assessment can be made of the equivalence of the system.

Once product has entered the territory of the EU with appropriate certification, it can be moved around freely with no further need for approval. All importers of organic products from outside the EU must be registered with an organic sector body and subject to at least annual inspection. By this means an audit chain is maintained.

TRACEABILITY

Wherever products are first certified, they should be accompanied thereafter by appropriate documentation and records, such that an audit trail is formed by which any organic food can be traced back to its source. Steps have to be taken to ensure that it is not adulterated along the way or that it is not part of an unapproved processing operation. During transit it has to be properly labelled and where appropriate must be packed and sealed to prevent switching. At any stage when this packaging is broken out of sight of the final customer or its nature is fundamentally changed by admixture or processing, or product is merely re-labelled, then that operation must be subject to inspection in the same way as the primary production. Thus, in the livestock sector, milk bottling plants and processing plants, egg packing stations, abattoirs and butchers shops among others require certification if they handle organic products.

This traceability has now to be applied to animal feedingstuffs. As a result of decisions to exclude all genetically modified materials from organic farming (CEC, 1999), and to ensure that there is no substitution of ingredients, all facilities producing compounded or blended feeds for organic stock must be inspected and certified. On-farm operations will be dealt with during normal farm inspections. This requirement applies not only to wholly organic feeds, but to any that are subsequently fed to organic stock. Operations dealing in straight feeds of organic origin must also be subject to inspection if an original consignment from a producer or importer is altered in any way e.g. by repackaging or splitting of a larger lot.

Ideally, conventionally produced straights (raw material feeds) should also be subject to checks but this is not currently considered to be obligatory. In parts of the country the low level of demand for feed for organic stock has meant that these procedures have not been fully enforced hitherto, but with the introduction of the EU Livestock Standards (CEC, 1999) it will now become obligatory. Any farmer feeding materials from non-certified sources runs the risk of his stock losing their organic status.

Record-keeping and traceability are the corner stones of organic verification. Analysis for traces of non-permitted materials has been seldom used to date. Absence of contaminants is no proof that they have not been used somewhere along the line and a positive test can result from accidental or environmental contamination rather than a conscious intent to defraud.

EFFECTIVENESS OF THESE CERTIFICATION PROCEDURES

Whilst it is believed that the above procedures are as robust as can reasonably be expected to be enforced, they cannot guarantee against attempted or even successful fraud. There are, however, additional checks in place, notably the extra inspections resulting from various accreditation schemes or quality control checks by multiple retailers on their suppliers. Neither should the effectiveness of neighbouring farmers or householders be underestimated. However this can be a two-edged sword, with false accusations being made against unpopular local people. That said, problems do arise. Many are sins of degree such as poor record keeping by farmers – something that UKROFS has constantly sought to improve. There have been isolated cases of more serious contraventions and the farmers concerned have been removed from registration. The very fact that these cases have come to light is reassurance, not only that the extensive effort that is put into control is worthwhile, but that it can also bring results.

EUROPEAN ORGANIC LIVESTOCK STANDARDS

As indicated above, until August 2000 all Member States were able to apply national livestock standards that needed to have no common features. In practice there was considerable commonality due to the common roots of organic farming but there were significant differences. Whilst the UK Standards

40

placed great emphasis on animal welfare issues other countries were far more concerned with not having conventional stock on organic land and maximising the use of organically-produced feedingstuffs. Consequently when it came to agreeing a common set of standards great difficulty emerged. The only way to get agreement was to include the provision that whilst all countries had to meet a minimum set of conditions they were free to introduce more stringent national rules if they wished.

After wide consultation UKROFS decided that, in implementing EU Regulation 1804/1999 in the UK, it would retain more stringent standards in certain aspects of organic livestock production. At the time of writing the overall EU situation is not clear. It is known that some other Member States such as France, are believed to have followed the UK example, others such as the Irish Republic have opted to introduce the precise EU Regulation.

ASPECTS WHERE UK STANDARDS DIFFER OR HAVE CHANGED

Probably the most crucial difference where the UK was not prepared to follow the consensus was the determination to maintain the principle that, apart from table poultry, if an animal is to be slaughtered for organic meat it must be born and raised on an organic farm according to organic standards. In the case of poultry because of the current lack of breeders working to organic standards, conventional chicks may be brought in, up to three days old. In many other countries other young animals from conventional farms can be brought on to an organic holding, be managed according to organic principles and subsequently be sold as fully organic. This will be re-considered by the Commission before 31 December 2003.

A number of other issues will come together eventually. However, some of the derogations such as the length of time that producers have to bring stocking rates in poultry housing down to the agreed values, can extend to 10 years. Currently, however, UK producers have only 5 years to conform, although this is subject to review.

Some areas where the rules have been relaxed in the UKROFS Standards as a result of the EU Regulation include: the possibility for a greater proportion of floor area to be slatted; the possibility for keeping stock without access to range for a greater proportion of their life and a relaxation on the rules for utilising common grazings. Conversely they maintain a ban on tethering stock and require that herbivores must have access to pasture at least during the growing season when conditions allow.

Provided that adequate separation can be demonstrated it may be possible to keep organic and non-organic livestock of the same species on the same farm provided they are on units which are physically, financially and operationally distinct. UKROFS has begun to provide guidance on what it believes constitutes such distinctness. However non-organic stock cannot be grazed on organic land, apart from a time-limited derogation of 120 days per year, and only then for specific management needs such as the alternating of cattle and sheep grazing to condition swards.

Whilst accepting that the standards proposed by the UKROFS Board should be incorporated into the necessary UK regulations, the Minister of Agriculture has asked officials to continue discussions with the poultry sector about actual and perceived differences between countries which could distort trade. In addition he has asked UKROFS to review the working of the livestock standards after 12 months.

REFERENCES

CEC (1989) *EN45011: General requirements for bodies operating product certification systems.* European Committee for Standardisation, CEC, Brussels.

CEC (1991). *Council Regulation No 2092/91 on organic production.* Official Journal of the European Communities, L198, 1-15.

CEC (1999) *Council Regulation No 1804/1999 supplementing Regulation No 2092/91 on organic production.* Official Journal of the European Communities, 42, L222, 1-28.

UKROFS (2000). *UKROFS Standards for Organic Livestock Production.* United Kingdom Register of Organic Food Standards, London, August 2000.

Chapter 5

Animal Health and Welfare in Organic Livestock Production

D. GRAY[1] and M. HOVI[2],
[1]SAC, Craibstone Estate, Bucksburn, Aberdeen AB21 6TB
[2]VEERU, University of Reading, Reading RG6 6AT

WHY IS ANIMAL HEALTH AND WELFARE IMPORTANT?

Animal production is an important feature of most organic farms. Animals form part of the rotation fundamental to many organic systems and are involved in recycling of nutrients through the use of animal wastes as organic fertiliser. It is generally accepted that animal well-being must be a fundamental attribute of organic livestock production. The IFOAM Basic Standards state that one of the basic principles of organic agriculture is "to give all livestock conditions of life with due consideration for the basic aspects of their innate behaviour" (IFOAM, 1998).

Organic systems are designed to achieve a balanced relationship between the components of soil, plant and animal. In general terms, each component is as important as the other in contributing to the overall effect. However, as sentient beings, animals have highly developed central nervous systems and behavioural needs, which place an added responsibility on the organic livestock producer. The production system is not sustainable if animals show evidence of pain, disease or distress as a result of an inadequate system. The need to prevent such situations forms the basis for the concepts of "Positive Health" and "Positive Welfare" in organic philosophy and practice. Health is not just the absence of disease and welfare is not just the provision of the five freedoms.

Apart from these philosophical considerations, there are also practical reasons why animal health and welfare must have a high priority in organic livestock production. When marketing organic products, the perception that organic livestock have been able to perform more of their natural behaviour and have benefited from higher welfare standards than animals on conventional farms is an important selling point. These perceptions have been reported among Swedish consumers (Holmberg, 2000). In a survey carried out in the UK, France, Italy, Germany and Ireland, consumers were reported to associate organic production with improved animal welfare (Harper and Henson, 1998).

Positive animal health in organic production is to be achieved without the use of conventional veterinary medicines on a routine basis. This provides a safeguard for the health of human consumers of organic livestock products. Such products are less likely to contain drug residues, such as antibiotics and hormones, as a result. Reduced levels of antibiotic resistance in indicator bacteria have been reported in organic broiler flocks compared to conventional ones (Heuer *et al.*, 2000). On the other hand, food safety must be safeguarded in relation to the presence of zoonotic organisms, such as *Salmonella*, *Campylobacter* and *Escherichia coli*. There have recently been accusations that organic products are more likely to be contaminated by such bacteria than conventional ones because of the reliance on animal wastes as fertilisers. There is little documented evidence to support this contention, although Heuer *et al.* (2000) found a higher prevalence of *Campylobacter* in organic broiler flocks than in conventional and extensive indoor flocks in Denmark.

Consumer perceptions of organic systems as being welfare-friendly and producing safe products must be reinforced by the reality of such systems in practice. The extent to which existing organic livestock standards can guarantee such aims needs to be considered.

ORGANIC STANDARDS: DO THEY DELIVER GOOD ANIMAL HEALTH AND WELFARE?

The legislation

In Europe during the 1990s, there were no common organic livestock standards in place. Each country developed and implemented its own standards within the general IFOAM guidelines.

This situation has changed within the European Union with the development and publication of a Council Regulation (EC) 1804/99 (CEC, 1999), which came into effect on the 24 August 2000. This Regulation, incorporated into the previous Regulation 2092/91 (CEC, 1991), provides the legislative framework for organic livestock standards in each of the EU member states. The Regulation dictates the minimum requirements although individual member states and individual certification bodies can retain and apply more stringent rules if they wish. In the United Kingdom, the Regulation has largely been incorporated directly into the UKROFS standards (UKROFS, 2000).

In relation to animal health and welfare, the Regulation confirms the philosophy of positive health and underlines the importance of good animal welfare. Disease prevention is to be achieved by:

- Selection of appropriate breeds or strains of animals.
- Application of animal husbandry practices appropriate to the requirements of each species, encouraging strong resistance to disease.
- Use of high quality feed, together with regular exercise and access to pasturage.
- Ensuring an appropriate stocking density.

In addition to the above, a number of restrictions on and penalties associated with the use of veterinary medicines are incorporated into the Regulation. These are designed to reduce the use of conventional veterinary medicines in particular. The treatment of clinically ill animals is obligatory but, for the first time, the Regulation requires that homeopathic or herbal remedies be used in preference to conventional medicines where the former are known to be effective in the treatment of a particular disease in the animal species in question.

In relation to animal welfare, the Regulation makes specific reference to the need for access to free range and, where housing is permitted, this "must meet the livestock's biological and ethological needs". There are specific minimum surface areas for indoor housing and outdoor exercise areas for each of the species covered by the Regulation. Other important aspects relating to welfare include nutritional standards, origin of animals and husbandry practices such as tethering, surgical operations and transport.

The issues

As can be seen from the above, the approach to positive animal health and welfare enshrined in European standards is based on a rational approach but with very little detail as to how the end is to be achieved. The production system and associated standards will not provide good animal health and welfare automatically.

There is a need for more detailed development of the principles stated and the application of known and novel solutions to overcome practical problems. As can be seen from the section on disease status in organic livestock below, there is no magic wand, which renders such animals immune from infectious and metabolic disease. Questioning the automatic assumption that organic animals are healthy and happy is a relatively recent phenomenon. Recently, issues such as housing systems, health plans, the use of antibiotics and transport and slaughter standards have been raised in connection with the development of EU livestock production standards. The Network for Animal Health and Welfare in Organic Agriculture (NAHWOA), a European research forum, has identified aspects, which highlight a few of the current difficulties (Thamsborg *et al.*, 2000):

- Organic farmers and certification bodies may be complacent about animal welfare, maintaining that organic farming, by definition equals good welfare.
- In certain countries, organic husbandry methods are seen as being "too natural" leading to animal welfare problems.
- Organic standards have often been developed as a result of pressure from consumer concerns rather than based on animal needs.

49

- The aims and aspirations of organic farming philosophy can sometimes conflict with animal health and welfare needs.
- Animal health is not always seen as an integral part of animal welfare on organic farms.

Animal welfare in organic livestock production systems

Animal welfare standards in organic livestock systems have been evaluated in various studies using different systems of quantitative animal welfare indices. Höring (1998) summarised a total of 15 of these studies carried out in Germany and Austria and concluded that organic systems achieve higher animal welfare standards than conventional systems, mainly due to the absence of tethering and/or caging of animals and due to the generous use of bedding. Mathes *et al.* (1998) reported high animal welfare scores for 510 organic dairy farms in 1996 and 1997. The scores out of 200 maximum were 159 and 162 in the two years. Roderick *et al.* (1996) also found that animal welfare was one of the major concerns and priorities among UK organic livestock farmers, who emphasised in their responses the efforts they made to maintain high levels of animal welfare on their farms.

The evaluation and assessment of animal welfare have been central issues in the development of organic livestock production systems in recent years. The organic standards have been criticised for poor provision of detailed animal welfare guidelines, and comparisons between individual country and certification body standards have been made (Schmidt, 2000). The introduction of a legal requirement for organic farms to achieve a certain scoring level in a welfare indexing system in Austria has given the issue added urgency (Bartussek, 2000).

Whilst the scoring system used in Austria (ANI 35L) has been criticised for its shortcomings in assessing health status (Bennedsgaard and Thamsborg, 2000), a need for the development of similar systems in other European countries has been recognised. The NAHWOA forum has identified the following needs for research and development in the assessment of animal welfare on organic livestock farms (Thamsborg *et al.*, 2000):

- The ANI 35L is accepted as a useful and versatile tool in identifying problem areas in animal housing conditions.
- The ANI 35L is also a good communication tool for contact with farmers and contains values other than purely economical.
- Whilst the ANI 35L is seen as very useful for scoring and categorising farms, it was emphasised that a more versatile assessment tool or series of assessment tools were needed.
- The following additions and improvements to the ANI 35L were proposed: Development and inclusion of practical and accurate animal health parameters; development and better inclusion of ways to measure stockmanship/human-animal interaction on the farm; development of practical systems of using body condition scoring as part of animal welfare assessment on farm; development of ways to include transportation and slaughter conditions into the index; and development of separate indices for production systems with minimum housing (e.g. Scottish hill farming).

Disease status in organic livestock production systems
The animal health situation on organic livestock farms has been surveyed in various studies. Halliday *et al.* (1991) and

51

Roderick *et al.* (1996) surveyed organic livestock farmers' disease management practices and their perception of disease levels on their farms in the UK. Both studies concluded that animal disease was not perceived to be a major problem on organic farms, and that there was a low level of conventional drug use. The specific disease problems highlighted by the reports were nutritionally-related reproductive problems in breeding stock, intestinal parasite infestation in grazing animals and fly strike in sheep.

In a longitudinal farm survey of eleven UK dairy farms in conversion to organic production (Weller and Cooper, 1996), mastitis was recognised as the main disease problem, with prevalence and incidence rates slightly higher, although not statistically significant, than those recorded on conventional farms.   Similar results were reported by Hovi and Roderick (2000), who also reported a significant reduction in the reliance on antibiotics in mastitis treatment, compared with matched conventional farms.

Lowman (1989) reported on the successful prevention of the most common diseases of beef cattle with homeopathic nosodes in a trial comparing organic and conventional management of beef cattle. An on-farm study of organic sheep (Newton, 1989) in Devon suggested no major disease problems in spite of the fact that there was no vaccination against clostridial diseases. The successful treatment of fly strike with iodine and control of parasites by grazing and management policies were also described. A summary of research results from organic dairy production systems in other countries is presented in Table 5.1.

Organic pig and poultry production systems are less well researched and data on disease levels are fairly anecdotal, due to the small number of farms in organic production. A survey of producer perceptions found that on a small number of organic UK pig farms the main concern was related to external parasites. Lameness and fertility problems, and high pig mortality, commonly associated with outdoor pig production, were considered as minor problems by the organic producers (Roderick and Hovi, 1999). In Austria, a survey of organic pig farms revealed higher levels of both external and internal parasitism than on conventional farms (Leeb and Baumgartner, 2000). The same survey also found high levels of antibodies to both parvovirus and porcine respiratory and reproductive syndrome virus, but these levels were similar to those found nationally in Austria.

A review of organic poultry production in the UK, suggests that coccidiosis, salmonellosis and ascites are potential health problems that may arise in free range conditions and when using poultry breeds that are not suited to organic production (Lampkin, 1997). More recently, the restrictions on the use of synthetic amino acids in poultry feeds and the unavailability of suitable breeds for outdoor production have been discussed as major barriers to high health and welfare status in organic poultry systems.

PREVENTIVE HUSBANDRY AS AN APPROACH TO HEALTH AND WELFARE PROBLEMS

Central to the strategy of positive health and welfare is the concept of preventive husbandry. This requires a positive effort on the part of the organic farmer and adviser to design systems, which prevent disease by means of the application of biological knowledge rather than reliance on medicine inputs. This concept can be applied to the prevention of infectious and

Table 5.1   Some key findings on production and health parameters in organic dairy herds

Country/Ref	Study design	Key results
Switzerland Augstburger et al., 1988	8 Organic 8 In conversion 8 Conventional 2 year study period	-Organic and in-conversion farms had higher culling rates (33.2 and 29.6 vs. 25.6%); -fully organic farms had lower longevity (4.14 and vs. 4.30 yrs), highest longevity on in-conversion farm at 4.43 yrs -Milk yields lower on organic and in conversion farms (4071 and 4470 vs. 5196 kg) -No significant difference in health and fertility parameters between the group
Germany Klenke, 1989	27 Organic 27 Conventional 3 year study period	-Organic farms had lower culling rates (20.8 vs. 23.3%) and milk yields (4558 vs. 5877 kg) -Organic cows had higher age at culling (5.85 vs. 5.43 yrs), longevity (3.18 vs. 2.88 yrs) and age at 1st calving (2.68 vs. 2.54 yrs) -No significant difference in calving intervals or lifetime milk yield
Germany Weber et al., 1993	1 experimental farm 151 Organic and 151 Conventional lactations	-Lactation yield lower in organically managed cows (by 871 kg/305 days), fat and protein content in milk non-significantly lower in organic cows; -milk production from forage higher in organic system (82 vs. 38%) -Energy deficiency observed in first 100 days of lactation in organic cows, clinical ketosis incidence not different form that among conventionally managed cows
Norway Ebbesvik, 1993	5 year study period 22 Organic 4 year study period	-Average annual milk yield per cow: 3300-5350 kg – significantly lower than national average -Mastitis, ketosis and milk fever treatment incidence significantly lower than national average, even when cows with similar yields were compared

Table 5.1 (cont.) Some key findings on production and health parameters in organic dairy herds

Country/Ref	Study design	Key results
Sweden Jonsson, 1996	1 experimental farm: 50 Organic cows 50 Conventional cows 6 year study period	-Milk yields 3% higher in the organically managed cows, milk fat higher and protein lower in organic group -Health parameters similar in the two groups
Germany Krutzinna et al., 1996	268 Organic One visit to farm to collect current and retrospective data	-Average milk yield/cow/lactation 4941 kg -Average age of cows 5.7 yrs with 3.2 lactations before culling -Average concentrate feeding 580 kg/cow/lactation -Mastitis main disease problem on 56% of farms, fertility disorder on 37 % and lameness on 26%
Canada Sholubi et al., 1997	8 Organic 4 year study period	-Small farms with average herd size of 48 cows (range 29-72); -average yield/cow/year 5882 litres (range 4328-7692 litres) -Average replacement rate 21%, average calving interval 390 days
Denmark Kristensen & Kristensen, 1998	13 Organic 18 Conventional Data from 3 year study period, simulation modelling	-Peak milk lactation lower but higher persistency in overall milk yields in organic cows -Lower incidence of mastitis in organic system -Herd structure dynamics: age structure and replacements rates similar in the two systems -If land use and feed supply only variables, reduced feed intake only variable in organic system, leading to lower milk yield and liveweight gain
Canada Allard & Pellerin, 1998	12 Organic 12 Conventional 3 month study period	-Milk yields 14% lower on organic farms; -milk composition similar in the two groups -Higher longevity on organic farms -Liveweight and body condition and health parameters similar in two groups of farms

parasitic disease as well as to the prevention of metabolic (production) disease, mineral and trace element deficiencies and poisonings.

Preventive husbandry uses information relating to the natural history of disease (epidemiology), immunity, nutrition, housing design, animal behaviour and stockmanship. In addition to farmer knowledge and experience there will almost certainly be a need to seek specialist advice in certain areas. Specific preventive husbandry strategies can be developed for individual farm situations and examples are given later. In general terms however, the husbandry measures are designed to promote animal health rather than disease within the three-way relationship of:

DISEASE CAUSING AGENT

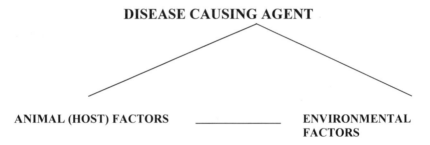

ANIMAL (HOST) FACTORS   **ENVIRONMENTAL FACTORS**

The strategies to be used will vary with the particular disease problem but there are some basic concepts and approaches, which apply to all situations and are directed at one or more points on the above triangle.

Affecting the disease-causing agent:

Examples of disease-causing agents are bacteria, viruses, parasites and metabolic and nutritional stress. Strategies to affect these agents can be divided into two:

-     Avoid contact with the animal host:

Biosecurity aspects (quarantine, animal purchase policy)
Break the life cycle of parasites by grazing management

- Reduce level of challenge to host:
Hygiene (working practices, disinfection, house design)
Reduced stocking density outside and housed
Grazing management for parasite control.

Affecting the animal factors (host/parasite relationship):

- Selection of breeds and strains suited to the local conditions and production system.
- Selection of breeds and individuals with natural resistance to disease.
- Provision of optimal nutrition at all stages of development and production cycles.
- Development of immunity as a result of natural exposure or vaccination if necessary.
- Reduction of stress due to adverse physical, social and environmental factors.

Affecting the environmental factors:

- Access to grazing for herbivores and other animals as appropriate.
- Provide shelter from weather and predators.
- Housing design to improve microclimate, reduce stress and allow natural behaviour.

Examples of preventive husbandry approaches

a)   Animal health plans

Retained in the UKROFS livestock standards is a requirement for organic farmers to develop a written animal health plan.

This plan should preferably be developed with the assistance of a veterinary surgeon and applies during the conversion period and beyond. This provides a formal framework for the evolution of a livestock system specific to each farm situation and which progressively requires less reliance on medicine inputs.

Various animal health plans and farm assurance schemes are being marketed by dairy companies, animal welfare organisations and veterinary bodies, but there are no clear guidelines for an "organic" animal health plan. Such guidelines are currently being developed in response to the UKROFS standard requirement by most certifying bodies. A "wish list" for an organic animal health plan is set out below in the hope that it will bear some resemblance to the plans that are likely to be adopted in the near future.

Whilst compliance with the organic standards is the legal cornerstone of organic production, the process of establishing a health plan on the farm should not be seen solely as an exercise to satisfy the organic inspectors. A well-designed and implemented animal health plan should be an excellent management tool that can save both money and time once established.

The main objectives of an animal health plan should be:

- To provide an animal health plan for organic livestock producers, so they are compliant with the UKROFS livestock standard requirements.
- To ensure compliance with best livestock practices and to promote positive animal health and welfare.
- To monitor the health and welfare status of organic livestock and preventive and curative methods used in

order to ensure the development of a pattern of health-building and disease- control measures that produces a system progressively less dependent on conventional veterinary medicinal products.

- To provide the farmer, the herdsperson/shepherd and the veterinarian, in whose care the animals are, with a useful tool to help them in their efforts to improve animal health and welfare on the farm.
- To provide the organic inspectors with a useful tool in the measurement and evaluation of health and welfare status of organic livestock farms.

The development of an animal health plan should ideally occur in two stages. Initially, livestock numbers, existing husbandry systems and methods, including routine medications and procedures, farm health security standards and recording system for disease and treatments should be evaluated and areas where changes need to be implemented should be identified. Based on a reliable method of estimation of the disease situation on the farm, disease problems or conditions that are considered to have an effect on the welfare status of the herd/flock should be identified, and a health plan and disease level targets for the next 12 months should be established.

The second stage of the animal health plan should be a continuous monitoring phase, including annual or twice yearly visits by the farm's veterinarian. During these visits, agreed monitoring and evaluation procedures are carried out and new targets for the next monitoring interval are set. This way the animal health plan becomes a dynamic document that changes continuously as the health situation of the herd/flock improves. The plan also provides the herdsperson/shepherd and the farm manager with useful feedback on the impact of the changes in husbandry methods, housing or treatment/prevention strategies that have been implemented on the farm.

b) *Integrated parasite control in ruminants*

Parasitic gastroenteritis (PGE) caused by roundworm parasites of sheep, cattle and goats can result in significant health and welfare problems. Poor growth rates, scour and even deaths can result. Organic farmers are faced with the problem of preventing such losses without the routine use of medicines (anthelmintics) to remove the parasites from the gut of the animal. Current control methods on organic farms are based on preventive husbandry methods, using knowledge of the life cycles of the parasites and of the ability of animals to develop immunity to them.

Gray (1999) states that current control measures are based on:
- Reducing exposure of the animals to worms, allowing them to develop immunity. This is particularly important in the case of young animals, which are most susceptible to the effects of the worms.
- Improving the ability of animals to develop such an immunity.

In practical terms, the first aim involves using a variety of grazing management strategies designed to reduce contamination of pastures with infective parasitic larvae or to move sheep off contaminated pastures before they become dangerous.

The classical example of this is the clean grazing system developed by the East of Scotland College of Agriculture (Rutter, 1975). This was designed to prevent PGE in sheep and cattle using a rotational grazing system in which one species of animal grazed the same area every three years. During the other two years, the area was either grazed by the other species or used for arable cropping or conservation. The theory behind this system is that parasites are in general species-specific and will not transfer between sheep and cattle and *vice versa*. In addition, the process of ploughing and cropping destroys parasitic larvae deposited on the pasture by the animals previously grazing the area. This system has not been taken up by conventional farmers to any great extent but is a practical proposition for organic farmers where mixed livestock enterprises and cropping rotations allow. Clean grazing does not entirely eliminate worm parasites however since certain worms (*Nematodirus battus* in particular) can infect both sheep and cattle and survive easily from one year to the next.

Other grazing management strategies can be used to reduce the level of exposure of animals to parasites on pasture. These include reducing the overall stocking densities of animals (Thamsborg *et al.*, 1996), mixed species grazing, for example, with sheep and cattle on the same pasture and alternate grazing between sheep and cattle on an annual basis.

These latter examples will not eliminate the risk of exposure to parasites and in these situations it is the young susceptible animal, which must be protected. This may involve using a strategic wormer dose for example treating ewes at lambing to prevent contamination of the pasture later in the summer or using "clean" silage or hay aftermaths or new leys for weaned lambs.

The second approach, which should be used in conjunction with the first approach described above, relates to increasing the innate or acquired resistance or tolerance of animals to parasites. Certain breeds or strains are reputed to be more resistant to the effects of parasites than others. Factual

61

information on this is sparse. However within a breed there is a wide range in susceptibility to parasites among individual animals (Stear *et al.*, 1998). Thus organic farmers should select a breed or cross which will be most suitable for their system, taking other factors such as prolificacy and hardiness into account. In addition, some organic farmers are selecting replacement breeding sheep on the basis of their likely resistance to worms. Currently, this is on the basis of faecal worm egg counts in young animals but in future more specific markers of innate resistance may become available.

The development of acquired resistance or tolerance to worm parasites in sheep is also influenced by nutritional factors (Coop and Kyriazakis, 1999). In particular, supplementation with metabolizable protein has been shown to affect the periparturient relaxation of immunity in ewes (Houdijk *et al.*, 2000). Trace elements such as copper, cobalt and selenium have been shown to be important in the development of immune function in cattle and sheep, and organic farmers should ensure that their systems provide adequate mineral and trace element nutrition.

Finally, monitoring of the success of the system being used should form an integral part of any strategy. In its simplest form, this will involve carrying out faecal worm egg counts on samples from a representative group of animals. The information from these samples can be used for several purposes; to justify the use of a strategic worming dose in recently lambed ewes, to decide if a group of lambs require treatment or to monitor progress when changes have been made to the system. Advice should be sought on the timing and number of samples required and in the interpretation of the results and need for action.

c) *Mastitis control*

Mastitis was identified early on as one of the major disease concerns for farmers converting to organic milk production. A survey of mastitis levels and mastitis control practices on organic dairy farms in England and Wales showed that, whilst mastitis levels were similar to those found on conventionally managed farms, the approaches to mastitis control differed significantly from those practised under conventional management (Hovi and Roderick, 2000). Organic dairy farmers used significantly less antibiotics and were less concerned about maintaining very low somatic cell count levels in their cows. Mastitis during the dry period, in the absence of routine antibiotic dry cow therapy, was a problem on some of the organic farms, whilst others managed to control mastitis well even during the dry period. It was, however, obvious in the study that both conventional and organic herdsmen failed to utilise recorded information on the farm to help them in their efforts to monitor and control mastitis.

Mastitis is one of the most common and distressing diseases on a dairy farm. Its prevention and effective treatment is vital on both animal welfare and milk quality grounds. On conventionally managed farms, prevention and control is often based on a broad approach that relies on five simple rules including routine use of antibiotics. The latter approach is unsuitable on organic farms and new approaches have been developed as a result of the above research.

Mastitis control on an organic dairy farm should be evidence-based and underpinned by a sound understanding of mastitis epidemiology on a particular farm. The following objectives for such an approach have been identified (Hovi and Roderick, 2000). During the conversion period the aim should be to:

- Create and maintain good recording and monitoring systems.
- Find out which mastitis pathogens are prevalent on the farm.
- Achieve acceptable mastitis levels by the end of the conversion period, particularly to minimise the presence of contagious mastitis in the herd.
- Learn to dry cows off without blanket antibiotic dry cow therapy.

Once the farm is fully organic, the following objectives should be adopted:

- To create a herd and an environment that enhances good udder health in a sustainable manner. This is to be achieved by, among other things, the encouragement, training and recognition of the stockperson, aiming at optimal rather than maximum milk yields, limiting antibiotic use to a minimum, but using them when they can be of help, breeding heifer calves from healthy cows with good longevity and conformation, maintaining good foot health and operating a closed herd policy, keeping the herd free of BVD (Bovine Viral Diarrhoea) and other contagious diseases that may impair immune function, keeping the milking machine serviced and following the rules of good milking hygiene and keeping the housing conditions as clean and dry as possible.
- To maintain minimum levels of contagious mastitis in the herd by sampling all cases of mastitis for bacteriology in order to identify the causative agents, by eradicating *Streptococcus agalactiae* infections as soon as they are identified and by practising a closed herd policy.

- To maintain environmental mastitis levels as low as possible by maintaining good housing hygiene and by allowing the minimum space (6 m²/cow) required for organic dairy cows.
- To maintain somatic cell counts (SCCs) at a level that provides a safe margin to the legal limit of saleable milk of 400,000 cells/ml. To achieve this a system of monthly individual cow SCC recording to identify chronically high SCC cows and to cull or treat these, withdrawing milk long enough after a case of clinical mastitis, even when alternative medication with no withdrawal period is used needs to be instigated. The aim should be to maintain the bulk tank SCC well below 300,000 cells/ml continuously.
- To identify and treat all cases of clinical mastitis promptly and with methods that also alleviate the pain associated with clinical mastitis.

FUTURE CHALLENGES

The future challenges relating to animal health and welfare in organic farming are varied, including exciting developments such as the implementation of findings from current and future research into preventive husbandry and animal behaviour, as discussed above. In the final part of this paper some of the challenges created by the complexity of organic objectives are discussed.

Conflicting aims

It has already been implied that the multiple aims of organic farming may in some situations be incompatible. The emphasis placed on certain aims may vary between countries and between individual consumers. It is well documented that consumers of animal products, when asked, will place animal welfare high on the list of those aspects they consider to be important when buying (Harper and Henson, 1998). However, animal welfare and health is often placed after environmental and food safety considerations by consumers (Soil Association, 1999). In situations where there is a conflict between two or more basic organic aims, how do the consumer and the organic movement make a choice? This debate over the relative value to be placed on animal welfare as opposed to environmental protection or human health is a relatively new one and is still evolving. There are aspects of the current organic standards where the potential for conflict exists. We discuss briefly two of these aspects: the use and non-use of conventional medicines and the potential risks to animal welfare, human health and the environment caused by free-range production systems.

Use of conventional medicines

The EU Regulation seeks to reduce the use of conventional veterinary medicines by the imposition of a variety of penalties such as extended withdrawal periods, increased requirement for record- keeping and the potential loss of organic status by individual animals or groups of animals. The purpose of these penalties is laudable; to safeguard human health and avoid exploitation of animals by intensive systems dependant on routine medicine inputs. However, it may be debatable as to whether the means of achieving it is the most acceptable from an organic viewpoint.

Our understanding of animal health and disease is by no means complete and there are specific situations where practical preventive husbandry methods do not exist which would result in an acceptable level of disease control. Examples are liver fluke disease in ruminants and external parasite infestations in all species. In such situations it may be necessary to use veterinary products in a limited strategic way to safeguard the health and welfare of animals, particularly under extensive conditions. Similarly, there is a lack of factual data relating to the safety and efficacy of herbal and homeopathic medicines. These are now to be used in preference to conventional veterinary medicines where they are known to be effective. Who decides whether a particular treatment is effective if the data are not available?

Finally, the EU Regulation limits the number of treatments which may be given to an animal or group of animals within a specific time period. Exceeding this limit results in the loss of organic status by that animal or group of animals. The economic and practical consequences of this are considerable and result in unfair pressure on organic farmers. As a result, the farmer may choose to withhold effective treatment resulting in poor animal welfare or, on the other hand, may choose to treat but not to record the use of a veterinary medicine, resulting in potential consumer safety concerns.

In the absence of long-term data from organically-managed livestock farms, it is difficult to say how real these concerns are. It may well be that organic husbandry leads to an integrated system at optimal production levels where the need to use any type of medicine seldom arises. On the other hand, situations may arise where animal welfare is genuinely jeopardised due to non-treatment. Development of evidence-based decision support systems for organic livestock farmers and efficient surveillance of health and welfare situations on organic farms via inspection and implementation of animal health plans are vital to avoid the latter scenario.

Risks associated with free-range systems of rearing livestock

Whilst rearing systems that allow full freedom of movement and access to outdoors for livestock are a fundamental requirement for organic production systems, certain concerns relating to free-range rearing have been expressed.

Risk associated with disease that can be transmitted from animals to humans (zoonoses) or situations where apparently healthy animals can act as carriers of pathogens that cause disease in humans is a concern for all types of livestock production. The public concerns relating to the BSE epidemic in the UK have emphasised this area of food safety and the subsequent mistrust of livestock production methods has benefited organic livestock production in terms of increased consumer awareness. In an organic production system, the transmission of the BSE agent would not have been possible, since the feeding of animal protein to ruminant animals has always been prohibited.

Concerns in relation to some other zoonotic pathogens have, however, arisen in organic production. These are mainly related to the use of animal wastes as fertiliser and to increased access of animals to their own faeces in free-range systems. A Danish study has found that whilst the levels of antimicrobial resistance in marker bacteria are significantly lower in organic outdoor broiler systems, the prevalence of *Campylobacter* in these flocks was high in comparison to conventional systems (Heuer *et al.*, 2000).

The suitability of modern hybrid breeds of monogastric livestock in particular for outdoor and free-range management systems has been discussed widely among the organic movement and efforts have been made within commercial systems to introduce breeds that are behaviourally suited for rearing conditions required by organic standards (van Putten, 2000; Bestman *et al.*, 2000; Hirt *et al.*, 2000). This is probably one of the greatest challenges facing the development of organic production systems which support positive health and welfare among monogastric livestock in a sustainable manner.

Addressing these problems is one of the major challenges of organic livestock production. Freedom to move and access to outdoors are vital for a sustainable system where animals can express their species-specific behaviour and fulfil their basic needs, and it is unlikely that this requirement will ever be removed from organic standards. It is therefore important to monitor potential problems and to seek solutions where real issues arise. Environmental and health monitoring of organic livestock production is necessary. Animal health plans and welfare assessment of organic livestock systems can again provide mechanisms for this.

Similarly, it will be important to develop free-range systems which minimise risks. Current research in the UK is looking at nitrate leaching from pig production systems which practice varied rotations. It is now widely accepted that only certain breeds of poultry are suitable for free-range systems, and an increasing amount of research is being carried out in all European countries to assess suitable housing systems for free range pigs and poultry. The challenge relating to the increased risk of free range livestock carrying zoonotic agents or agents that might cause disease in humans needs to be investigated in a risk factor analysis. This will allow the development of management systems which minimise the potential risk and allow solutions based on husbandry rather that medicinal control.

REFERENCES

Allard, G. and Pellerin, D. (1998) L'approche biologique pour produire du lait autrement...Ca donne aussi des resultats a l'etable. *Producteur de lait Quebecois.* 18: 44-47.Anon (1999) Council Regulation (EC) No 1804/1999. *Official Journal of the European Communities*, L222: 1-28.

Augstburger, F., Zemp, J. and Heusser, H. (1988) Vergleich der Fruchbarkeit, Gesundheit und Leistung von Milch-kuhen in biologisch und konventinell bewirts-chafteten Betrieben. *Landwirtschaft Schweiz.* 1 (7): 427-431.

Bartussek, H. (2000). How to measure animal welfare? The idea of an animal needs index (ANI-35L): a practical tool for assessing farm animal housing conditions on farm level in respect to animals' well being and behavioural needs - Austrian experiences. In:*Diversity of livestock systems and definition of animal welfare, Proceedings, 2nd NAHWOA Workshop, Cordoba, 8-11January 2000*. 135-142.

Bennedsgaard, T. and Thamsborg, S. M. (2000). Comparison of welfare assessment in organic dairy herds by the TGI200-protocol and a factor model based clinical examinations and production parameters. In: *Diversity of livestock systems and definition of animal welfare, Proceedings of the 2nd NAHWOA Workshop, Cordoba, 8-11, January 2000*. 143-150.

Bestman, M., Beukenkamp, M. and Baars, T. (2000). Welfare of beaked laying hens. In: *Proceedings 13th International IFOAM Scientific Conference, Basel 28-31 Aug.* 362.

CEC (1991). *Council Regulation No 2092/91 on organic production*. Official Journal of the European Communities, L198, 1-15.

CEC (1999) *Council Regulation No 1804/1999 supplementing Regulation No 2092/91 on organic production.* Official Journal of the European Communities, 42, L222, 1-28.

Coop, R. L. and Kyriazakis, I. (1999) Nutrition-parasite interaction. *Veterinary Parasitology,* 84, 187-204.

Ebbesvik, M. (1993) Melkeproduksjon i ökologisk landbruk. För, föring, helse og avdrott. *Meieriposten* 11: 316-317.

Gray, D. (1999) Control of parasites in upland sheep production systems. In: The 11th National Conference on Organic Food and Farming, Royal Agricultural College, Circencester, 8-10 January 1999. Abstract.

Halliday, G., Ramsay, S., Scanlan, S. and Younie, D. (1991) A survey of organic livestock health and treatment. The Kintail Land Research Foundation. 29 pp.

Harper, G. C. and Henson, S. J. (1998). *Consumer Concern about Animal Welfare and the Impact on Food Choice: comparative literature review.* EU FAIR CT98-3678.

Heuer, O. E., Pedersen, K., Andersen, J. S. and Madsen, M. (2000). Prevalence of thermophilic Campylobacter and antimicrobial susceptibility patterns of zoonotic and indicator bacteria from organic and conventional broilers in Denmark. A poster presentation at the Nordic Veterinary Mote, Reykjavik, 4-5 October 2000.

Hirt, H., Hordegen, P. and Zeltner, E. (2000) Laying hen husbandry: group size and use of hen runs. In: *Proceedings 13th International IFOAM Scientific Conference, Basel 28-31 August, 2000.* 363.

Holmberg, H. (2000). Rapport konsumentundersokning om ekologiska produkter/KRAV. LUI Marknadsinformation AB.

Houdijk, J. G. M., Kyriazakis, I., Jackson, F. Huntly, J. F. and Coop, R. L. (2000) Can an increased intake of metabolizable protein affect the periparturient relaxation in immunity against Teladorsagia circumcincta in sheep? Veterinary Parasitology, 91: 43-62.

Hovi, M. and Roderick, S. (2000) Mastitis and mastitis control strategies in organic milk production. *Cattle Practice*, 8:3, 259-264.

Höring, B. (1998) Tiergerechtheit und Tiergesundheit in ökologishc wirtschaftenden Betrieben. *Dtsch. Tierärtzl. Wschr.* 105, 313-321.

IFOAM (1998) International Federation for Organic Agricultural Movements. IFOAM Basic Standards for Organic Production and Processing, IFOAM Publications, Germany.

Jonsson, S. (1996) *Ekologisk mjölkproduktion - de första sex åren efter omställning.* Fakta-Husdjur 8. 4 pp.

Klenke, B. (1989) *Untersuchungen in Rinderheerden auf Betrieben mit unterschedlicher Wirtschaftsweise unter besonderer Berucksichtigung der Milchleistung, Gesundheit und Fruchbarkeit.* Thesis - Tierärtzliche Hochschule Hannover, Germany. 109 pp.

Kristensen, T. and Kristensen, E. S. (1998). Analysis and simulation modelling of the production in Danish organic and conventional dairy herds. *Livestock Production Science* 54: 55-65.

Krutzinna, C., Boehncke, E. and Herrmann, H. J. (1996) Organic milk production in Germany. *Biological Agriculture and Horticulture.* 13: 351-358.

Lampkin, N. (ed.) (1997). Organic poultry production. University of Wales. 77 pp.

Leeb, T. and Baumgartner, J. (2000) Husbandry and health of sows and piglets on organic arms in Austria. In: *Proceedings 13th International IFOAM Scientific Conference, Basel 28-31 August, 2000.* 361.

Lowman, B. G. (1989). A comparison of organic and conventional management of beef cattle. In: *Organic Meat Production in the 90's.* Chalcombe Publications. 19-31.

Mathes, H. D., Freitag, J. and Goesmann, M. (1998) Entwicklung und Anwendnung eines Tiergerechtheitindexes für die Freilandhaltung von Rindern. *Archiv für Tierzucht*, 41: 573-582.

Newton, J. (1989). A case study of an organic sheep farm. In: In: *Organic Meat Production in the 90's.* Chalcombe Publications. 33-40.

Roderick, S. Short, N. and Hovi, M. (1996) Organic livestock production – Animal health and welfare research priorities. Technical Report – VEERU, University of Reading. 29 pp.

Roderick, S. and Hovi, M. (1999). Animal health and welfare in organic livestock systems: identification of constraints and priorities. A report to the Ministry of Agriculture, Fisheries and Food. 65 pp.

Rutter, W. (1975) Sheep from grass. Bulletin No. 13, East of Scotland Agricultural College, Edinburgh.

Schmid, O. (2000) Comparison of European organic livestock standards with national and international standards - problems of common standards development and future areas of interest. In: *Diversity of livestock systems and definition of animal welfare, Proceedings of the 2nd NAHWOA Workshop, Cordoba, 8-11 January 2000.* 63-75.

Sholubi, Y. O., Stonehouse, D. P. and Clarke, E. A. (1997) Profile of organic dairy farming in Ontario. *American Journal of Alternative Agriculture.* 12: 133-139.

Soil Association (1999) The organic food and farming report 1999, 25-29, Soil Association, Bristol

Stear, M. J., Bairden, K., Bishop, S. C., Gettinby, G., McKellar, Q. A., Park, M., Strain, S. and Wallace, D. S. (1998) The processes influencing the distribution of parasitic nematodes among naturally infected lambs. Parasitology, 117: 165-171.

Thamsborg, S. M., Jorgensen, R. J., Waller, P. J. and Nansen, P. (1996) The influence of animal density on gastrointestinal nematodes of sheep over a two year grazing period. Veterinary Parasitology, 67: 207-224.

Thamsborg, S. M., Hovi, M. and Baars, T. (2000). What to do about animal welfare in organic farming? A report on the animal welfare discussion at the 2nd NAHWOA workshop. In: *Diversity of livestock systems and definition of animal welfare, Proceedings of the 2nd NAHWOA Workshop, Cordoba, 8-11, January 2000.* 161-165.

UKROFS (2000) UKROFS Standards for Organic Food Production. *Standards for Organic Livestock and Organic Livestock Products.* United Kingdom Register of Organic Food Standards.

Van Putten, G. (2000). An ethological definition of animal welfare with special emphasis on pig behave. In: *Diversity of livestock systems and definition of animal welfare, Proceedings of the 2nd NAHWOA Workshop, Cordoba, 8-11, January 2000.* 120-134.

Von Weber, S., Pabst, K., Ordolff, D., Gravert, H. O. (1993) Fünfjahrige Untersuchungen zur Umstellung auf ökologische Milcherzeugung. 2. Mitteilung: Milchqualität und Tiergesundheit. *Zuchtungskunde* 65: 338-347.

Weller, R. F. and Cooper, A. (1996) Health status of dairy herds converting from conventional to organic farming. *Veterinary Record,* 139: 141-142.

Chapter 6

Organic Grassland: The Foundation Stone of Organic Livestock Farming

D. YOUNIE
SAC, Craibstone Estate, Bucksburn, Aberdeen AB21 9YA

INTRODUCTION

In organic farming, the components of the whole farm system interact closely and grassland plays the central role in this intricate web, including the arable cropping phase. Grassland is important particularly in relation to nitrogen supply via its influence on N-fixation, soil organic matter, structure and biological activity and it also has a major role to play in restricting the build-up of arable weeds and soil-borne crop diseases in arable rotations. Ruminant livestock share this central role with grassland on most successful organic farms, and the success of the livestock enterprise is intimately tied up with the management and productivity of the grassland.

TEMPORARY AND PERMANENT GRASSLAND

Where regular ploughing is possible and the climate permits arable cropping, a rotational system of temporary grassland production is preferable to permanent grassland, for a number of reasons:

   a) Ensures a high clover content can be maintained in swards.

b) Provides clean grass, uncontaminated with worm larvae, annually for young stock.
c) Minimises the build-up of, and provides an opportunity for control of, perennial grassland weeds such as docks.
d) Permits the exploitation by arable crops of soil fertility built up under the grass/clover ley.
e) Provides an opportunity to produce arable crops for sale and/or livestock feeding.

A ley grassland policy has the disadvantage of increased seed and establishment costs, but this is a cost the farmer has to pay for the advantages listed above. Another potential disadvantage is the increased risk of nitrogen leaching loss following ploughing up the ley, but this can be minimised by ploughing in late winter, for a spring crop, rather than ploughing in autumn. In addition, ploughing of the ley will occur only once during the rotation.

MANAGEMENT OBJECTIVES

Grassland management objectives on organic farms are not necessarily prioritised in the same order as on conventional farms. Whilst maximising herbage and livestock output per hectare may be the common overall aim, the restrictions of the organic standards in relation to plant nutrient inputs and routine veterinary treatment of livestock mean that strategies to maintain high animal health status and to maintain soil nutrient status are equally, if not more important, than maximising herbage output per hectare in the short-term. In fact, although many conventional farmers considering converting to organic farming are mostly concerned about maintaining herbage productivity, in systems with a high proportion of young stock such as calves and lambs, it may not be herbage production which forces a limit on stocking rate, but the risk of parasitic gastro-enteritis caused by worm invasion.

THE ROLE OF GRASSLAND MANAGEMENT IN ENHANCING LIVESTOCK HEALTH

Grassland management has a major influence on livestock health through:
  a) The quality and quantity of nutrition obtained from grassland, and
  b) the potential adverse effects of worm invasion and bloat.

Worm control

The extent of worm larval challenge which a contaminated pasture presents to grazing animals will depend on:
  a) The level of contamination in the sward at the start of the grazing period (e.g. in spring).
  b) The level of egg deposition by grazing animals during the current grazing period.
  c) The degree to which weather conditions favour the development of eggs and larvae during the current grazing period.

Young animals are more susceptible to lungworm and stomach worms than adults. Because of this, the build-up of pasture contamination is much faster when the sward is grazed by young, infected animals rather than mature animals. As animals mature, they develop immunity to the parasites on exposure to low or moderate levels of parasite challenge. However, mature animals may lose their immunity during periods of stress e.g. ewes during lambing which may excrete large numbers of stomach worm eggs - the peri-parturient egg rise.

77

Potential for worm control by grazing management

A number of grassland management strategies can be employed in order to minimise the risk of infection by endoparasites in cattle and sheep. These include:

Mechanism	Practice	Comment
Dilution	Lower stocking rates Mixed species grazing Mixed age groups grazing	Worm challenge on susceptible grazing animals is **diluted** by a lower stocking rate or by the presence of another (immune) species or (immune) adult stock of the same species see below
Evasion	Clean pastures ready before the expected rise in pasture infectivity i.e. late June (sheep) or mid July (cattle) Swards grazed by another species in spring Use of silage or hay aftermaths Use of new grass reseeds Use of annual forage crops	Worm challenge on susceptible grazing animals is evaded by **moving** animals from **contaminated pastures** to clean pastures (not grazed same year by the same species)
Prevention	Use of new grass reseeds Use of silage or hay aftermaths Use of annual forage crops Late lambing (*Nematodirus*) Yearly alternation between livestock species	Worm challenge is prevented by introducing **uninfected stock** to clean pastures every year

The yearly alternating clean grazing system is perhaps the most widely recognised clean grazing system. In this system, each field is managed according to the following three-year rotation:

Year 1 →	Year 2 →	Year 3 →
Sheep	Silage	Cattle

The system can be refined further, for example, by moving weaned lambs in late summer to silage aftermaths, or moving some cattle in late summer to graze together with dry ewes after weaning. This system is only possible where each field is sufficiently flat for cutting for hay or silage. However, even where cutting is not possible, e.g. on undulating permanent pasture, a two-year rotation between cattle and sheep will also help to minimise the worm challenge.

The strategy adopted on any one farm will depend on the physical resources of the farm and on the farming system employed. However, worm problems will be minimised on farms which are able to employ:

a)   a mixed ley/arable system;
b)   based on temporary leys rather than permanent grassland;
c)   with more than one livestock species;
d)   land quality which allows silage to be made on every field.

Where physical and financial resources permit, organic livestock farmers should adopt such a system, or at least as many elements of it as possible, in order to minimise worm problems in young stock. The availability of new reseeds each year will provide a source of clean pasture in spring for grazing susceptible young stock. If silage can be made from all fields and arable crops can be grown, there is maximum flexibility to move susceptible young stock as the season progresses, to silage aftermaths or arable cropping fields in late season, and so evade the build-up in worm challenge. With more than one livestock species on the farm, the overall stocking rate of susceptible animals is reduced and options for mixed species grazing or yearly alternating grazing are available.

Some farm types may have very restricted options because of the limited physical resources of the farm. An example is the sheep-only farm on marginal land, which may have limited land suitable for ploughing or grass conservation and is therefore not suitable for a cattle enterprise. On such a farm it is difficult to adopt a clean grazing system.

The only grassland management option may be to restrict stocking rate of sheep, although this may have consequences in terms of poor utilisation of herbage and a subsequent drop in forage quality. In this situation the farmer also needs to introduce a system of regular faecal egg counts in order to predict when a rise in worm infection is about to occur and hence when anthelmintic treatment is necessary, although frequent necessity for anthelmintic treatment will not be acceptable to the organic certification body. Introduction of a breeding programme to improve worm resistance in the sheep stock will also be necessary in this situation.

Herbage quality and livestock health

The trace element (TE) content of the herbage is largely determined by the parent material of the soil. Nevertheless, management decisions can affect trace element content. In particular, a high soil pH will reduce the uptake of trace elements in the herbage. A pH of 5.8 to 6.0 should be the target pH, therefore, rather than pH 6.2 to 6.5. Given that there is a limited supply of trace elements in the soil, the higher the yield of the crop, by dilution the lower will be the TE content of the herbage in percentage terms. Thus perennial ryegrass, which is relatively high yielding, tends to have a lower copper content than many other species. Herbage species which have a deeper root system may have a high TE content.

A number of herb species have deep tap roots and have the potential to explore deeper soil layers than conventional herbage species, and potentially make available an enhanced supply of nutrients (Swift *et al.*, 1990; Wilman and Derrick, 1994). This potential advantage of herbs has been demonstrated in practice, in the animal, by Younie *et al.* (1997), with weaned lambs grazing pure stands of chicory or perennial ryegrass (Table 6.1).

Table 6.1 Effect of pure stands of chicory (C) or perennial ryegrass without (PRG) or with a Cosecure+ bolus (PRG/CS), on the blood mineral status of grazing lambs (from Younie *et al.*, 1997).

Blood constituent	C	PRG	PRG/CS	Sig.
Ca (mmol/l)	3.15	3.01	3.16	*
PO_4 (mmol/l)	2.64	2.43	2.38	NS
Na (mmol/l)	144.3	137.5	141.6	NS
Mg (mmol/l)	0.99	0.91	0.98	*
Cu (μmol/l)	10.25	7.55	11.49	*
GSHPx (units/ml RBC)	19.38	17.38	20.0	NS
$VitB_{12}$ (ng/l)	965	705	929	***

+ Administered orally as a sustained-release intra-ruminal source of supplementary Co, Se and Cu.
* = $P<0.05$; *** = $P<0.001$.

Deficiencies of calcium and magnesium in the diet, potentially causing milk fever and hypomagnaesemia, are not normally as serious in the organic situation as in the conventional situation. This is because the phenomenon of luxury uptake of K in herbage is less likely to occur since spring applications of N and K fertilisers/manures are not usually made to grazed grass. Nevertheless, the risk should be borne in mind, especially if spring slurry applications are made to grazed grass on a clay soil, which will have an inherently high K availability.

In organic ruminant diets, grassland is the primary source of protein as well as energy. Because of the restricted choice of purchased protein sources, it is essential to maximise the amount of home-produced protein. Thus, there is a nutritional need to maximise clover content in swards, as well as an agronomic need (see below). The crude protein (CP) content of silage will vary with the clover content and the cutting date.

Early cut pure clover swards can have CP contents in excess of 20% of the dry matter (DM), while late cut swards with moderate clover content may be as low as 12 to 13% CP. In mixed grass/white clover swards, the proportion of clover in the DM in a first cut silage crop increases to a maximum around the second or third week of May and thereafter declines as the grass component starts to flower (Younie and Giordano, 1993). Thus, in the UK the second or third week of May is probably the best date to cut if a high digestibility, high CP silage is the aim.

In late summer, the white clover content of grazed pasture can be as high as 60 to 70% in the DM and soil nitrate N content is high. This leads to an excess of rumen degradable protein (RDP) in grazing animals. Much of this passes through the animal as urine and increases the risk of loss of N to the environment via ammonia volatilisation and nitrate leaching. In addition the excess of protein over energy in the diet can lead to health problems in productive animals such as high yielding dairy cows. In these situations the high protein intake should be balanced by buffer feeding a high energy forage such as whole-crop cereal silage (Van Eekeren, 2000).

Bloat

Bloat will occur in cattle (but almost never in sheep) grazed on rank (10 to 20cm) swards with a very high clover content. The risk of bloat is greatest in August and September, when clover content of swards is highest. Silage and hay aftermaths pose the highest risk, especially when coupled with low DM herbage, e.g. on damp, dewy mornings in September. Bloat rarely occurs in early summer. The occurrence of bloat can be predicted to some extent, therefore, and steps taken to minimise the risk. Cattle should never be turned on to rank clovery swards. They should be turned on to aftermaths immediately after the crop has been lifted, so that the clover grows to the cattle. If it is impossible to avoid turning cattle on to high-risk swards, they should be well fed before transfer, on a dry afternoon, when the herbage is also dry. In very high-risk situations, poloxalene bloat preventative should be fed for two days prior to transfer and for as long afterwards as the high risk period lasts.

ENHANCING HERBAGE PRODUCTION

The main factors affecting herbage production per hectare are:
  a) Botanical composition of the sward, and
  b) growing conditions: nutrient supply and environmental conditions (soil moisture supply and temperature).

The farmer can do little about rainfall and temperature, but can have a major influence on the nutrient supply to and botanical composition of the sward.

Botanical composition: seed mixtures

Nitrogen is the most important crop nutrient and so herbage legumes such as clovers are the driving force in organic systems, because of their ability to fix large amounts of atmospheric nitrogen. The quantity of N fixed is directly dependent on the proportion of clover in the sward. Thus, a major objective should be to **maximise the clover content** of the sward.

White clover is by far **the most appropriate and widely used forage legume** for organic farming systems in temperate maritime climates, because of its adaptability to a range of management and soil fertility conditions. It is persistent, is not demanding in terms of soil pH and drainage conditions, and can be used for management regimes ranging from continuous sheep grazing (for which small-leaved varieties are most suitable) to lax defoliation, including cutting (for which larger leaved varieties are most suitable).

Red clover is also undemanding in terms of soil conditions and is highly productive, but is not persistent nor well-suited to grazing, and should only be sown in mixtures intended for short-term leys (up to three years), primarily for cutting. It is probably the best species for use as a one or two year green manure. Lucerne and sainfoin also have considerable potential as crops for conservation, but are suitable only for soils with a relatively high pH (above 7) and, in the case of lucerne, good drainage.

The agronomic characteristics of the companion grass species are also important in enhancing sward productivity. Although

perennial ryegrass has been criticised as being more appropriate for intensive high N systems than for organic or low-input systems, **it is undoubtedly the most suitable species for ley farming in temperate maritime conditions**, given its ease of establishment, yield potential, persistence, and quality characteristics. Tetraploid varieties are known to promote a higher clover content in the sward than diploid varieties, because of their more open growth habit.

Traditionally, organic farmers have often regarded secondary or indigenous grass species and forbs with approval, either in unsown pastures and field boundaries or sown in complex seed mixtures. Improved livestock nutrition and health are the reasons normally given. Herbs also tend to be more drought resistant than grasses and their tap root systems may also lead to a more open soil structure. Despite these potential advantages, forage herbs have been largely overlooked in practice, even in organic farming (Foster, 1988). This is changing to some extent, at least in New Zealand and Australia, where breeding effort has led to the commercial release of varieties of **chicory** and **ribwort** (Moloney and Milne, 1993).

Perhaps the main reason for the low level of use of forage herbs is their generally low contribution to sward biomass, largely resulting from low seed rates, poor establishment and persistence. This may be due, at least in part, to their inability to persist under intensive management regimes involving frequent utilisation by cutting and grazing - regimes to which vigorously tillered grass species such as perennial ryegrass are ideally suited. New thinking is also required in relation to the most appropriate companion species and mixtures for forage herbs. Umrani (1998) has shown that perennial ryegrass, with its vigorous, densely tillered growth habit, is a major competitor. It significantly reduced root length, root weight and shoot weight of individual herb plants. The upright and less well tillered growth habit of timothy is less competitive and, coupled with the N-fixing ability of white clover, makes for a more suitable mixture, perhaps **sown in strips** or as separate swards, with the main bulk of the field sown to a ryegrass-based mixture. Of course the composition of mixtures needs to be designed with the proposed management regime in mind, and much work requires to be done to develop reliable and persistent herb-based mixtures for a range of organic management situations.

Typical seed mixtures for organic grassland are in Table 6.2.

Table 6.2   Typical seed mixtures for organic leys (kg/ha)

	Two-year ley, two cuts silage, aftermath grazing	4 to 6 year ley, cutting, grazing	Long-term ley, mainly grazing
Hybrid ryegrass (T)	5		
Intermediate perennial ryegrass (T)	10	10	
Late perennial ryegrass (T)		14	28
Timothy		4	
Red clover	10		
Small-leaved white clover		1.0	
Medium-leaved white clover		1.5	1.5
Large-leaved white clover		1.5	2.5
Total	25	32	32

T = Tetraploid.

Botanical composition: Clover establishment

Given that clover is the most important component of the sward, the primary objective in establishing the sward must be to achieve rapid and effective establishment of the clover. For both white and red clovers, the best method of establishment is by direct sowing (i.e. without a cover crop), in spring, on a ploughed seedbed (Figure 6.1).

Figure 6.1 Effect of undersowing, date of sowing and N supply on establishment of clover (Younie *et al.*, 1984)

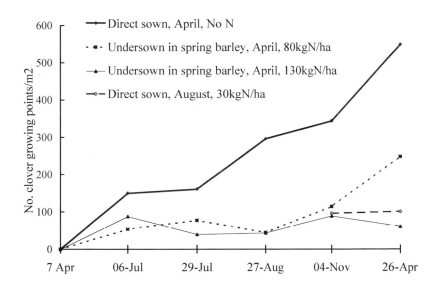

In comparison, undersowing with a cereal delays the development of both clover and grass plants, although it can still give satisfactory establishment since second or third organic cereal crops are not always vigorous, competitive crops.

Generally the most unreliable method of clover establishment is sowing in late summer/autumn, because of the risk of loss by frost heave of poorly rooted and anchored clover seedlings during winter. Clearly, this risk is worst in areas where growing seasons are short and winters are severe.

In some situations, at least during conversion, there may be a need to **oversow clover** into existing swards in order to improve clover content, rather than to undertake a complete reseed. This situation is sub-optimal for the germinating clover seedling: sown on the surface, surrounded by very competitive, well established plants. The type of machine which is used to deliver the seed is largely irrelevant - the two most important factors in successful oversowing are:

a) An adequate soil moisture supply, and
b) control of the competition from the existing sward.

These requirements are best met by broadcasting the seed in early spring when there is still plenty of moisture in the soil into a very short, well-grazed sward, and to continue grazing right through the first season to control the competition.

Botanical composition: Maintenance of clover content

The four factors which have greatest influence on white clover content in an established sward are:

a) Soil nutrient content, in particular pH, phosphorus (P) and potassium (K) content;
b) avoidance of application of soluble N;
c) autumn or winter grazing to encourage clover content;

d) cutting for hay or silage in mid-season to increase stolon density.

Application of soluble N is not a major issue in the organic situation, and it will not be possible to cut every sward in mid-season. However, it is vital that organic farmers maintain soil pH, P and K levels, and that swards are grazed down hard, ideally by November/December. This removes grass cover, allows light in to the light receptors on clover stolons, and encourages subsequent stolon branching (Laidlaw *et al.*, 1992).

Red clover grows from a crown in an upright, tufted growth habit. It does not have the same powers of recovery and recolonisation as a stoloniferous species such as white clover. Inevitably, therefore, the plant density of red clover and the sward productivity will decline after the first year. The major factors which are implicated in loss of red clover plants are stem eelworm and fungal invasion of the crown (e.g. by *Fusarium*) brought on by physical damage to plants by grazing animals, especially sheep, and passage of vehicles. It follows, therefore, that persistence of a satisfactory stand of red clover is more likely to be achieved by selecting varieties which have a high resistance to eelworm, by avoiding overgrazing by sheep, and by minimising the passage of vehicles on the sward.

Botanical composition: weed control

Control of perennial weeds such as dock and creeping thistle presents a major agronomic challenge in long-term organic grassland, since herbicide use is prohibited. A combination of different approaches is likely to be required. Where the site is ploughable, adoption of a ley/arable system using, say, 3 to 5 year leys rather than permanent grassland, is likely to prevent the problem developing because of the regular ploughing and disturbance to dock plants. Continuous cutting for hay or silage should be avoided if possible because a dock infestation becomes worse (and grass yield falls) more rapidly under a cutting than under a grazing management (Figure 6.2).

Figure 6.2 Change in relative yield of dock-infested swards over time, under cutting or grazing management. (Initial dock density two plants/m²) (Extracted from Courteny, 1985)

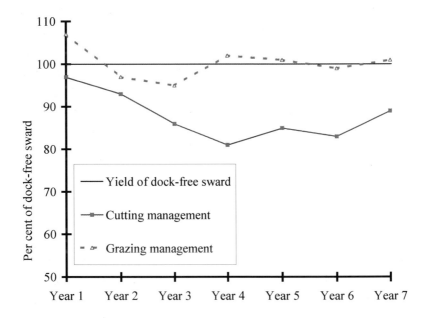

Regular topping of grazed swards, and soil aeration to improve grass growth and cause physical damage to dock roots, may also limit the increase in dock density (Hopkins *et al.*, 1997).

When dock infested grassland is to be reseeded, rotovating the turf to a depth of 8 to 10cm in June, followed by dessication for 8 to 10 weeks before ploughing and establishment of the next crop, has been successful (Welsh, 1995). Perhaps a more active degree of dock tap root destruction and continued surface disturbance would be achieved by grazing with unringed sows. Certainly this is one of the main attractions of an organic pig enterprise.

As implied above, it would be preferable to introduce an intermediate arable crop or winter cover crop before reseeding the grass sward. The additional cultivation involved is likely to reduce dock density further, provided that ploughing and not surface cultivation is used for the establishment of the intermediary crops, since surface cultivation generally leads to more weed germination than ploughing. Forage rye may be a suitable winter cover crop in this scenario, since it is reputed to have allelopathic effects. When the new sward is eventually rcsown, Hopkins *et al* (1997) have suggested that high grass/clover seed rates can reduce dock infestation at sward establishment.

Crop nutrient supply: Nitrogen

As indicated above, N is the single most important nutrient for most crops, including grassland. The ultimate source in organic systems is biological N fixation, and the amount generated is directly dependent on the clover content of the sward.

Whitehead (1995) reported amounts of fixed N ranging from 0 to 445 kg N/ha/annum, with an overall average of 152 kg N/ha/annum. The lower end of this range is associated with soils of high potential for N mineralisation, continuous grazing management and smaller leaved white clovers, whilst the upper end of the range is associated with soils of low potential for N mineralisation, cutting or rotational grazing management, large-leaved white clovers and red clover or lucerne (e.g. Davies and Hopkins, 1996).

The level of N fixation is primarily dependent on the clover content of the sward, particularly in the early years of a ley (e.g. Van der Meer and Baan Hofman, 1989). Kristensen *et al* (1995) have used clover ground cover as the basis for estimating the amount of atmospheric N fixed in grass-clover systems (Table 6.3).

Table 6.3 **Effect of clover content and age of ley on estimated N-fixation in organic grass-clover leys** (kg N/ha/annum. From Kristensen *et al*, 1995).

Clover content (% ground cover)		10 to 29	30 to 49	Above 49
Clover content (% in dry matter)		3 to16	17 to 29	Above 29
Age of ley (years):	1st, 2nd	80	157	248
	3rd, 4th and 5th	47	84	128

In addition to contributing to herbage growth, a proportion of the atmospherically fixed N is stored in roots and stubble or is immobilised in soil organic matter, i.e. it contributes to the longer term build up of soil organic matter and soil N status. Simultaneously, a proportion of the N in the soil organic pool is mineralised and becomes available for uptake by pasture plants. As the supply of N from mineralised soil organic matter increases (e.g. in the later years of a ley), the relative contribution from N-fixation to the overall supply of N to the sward declines (Younie, 1992; Davies and Hopkins, 1996), as implied also in the data of Kristensen *et al* (1995) in Table 3.

The farmer can also optimise the amount of mineralised soil N by avoiding soil compaction by grazing animals and by machinery (e.g. manure application and silage harvesting machinery). Compaction can reduce mineralisation of N by 30% (Hansen, 1995). Avoidance and alleviation of compaction (e.g. by regular sub-soiling) are an important means of improving N supply to the grass sward particularly on naturally poor-draining soils.

Crop nutrient supply: Phosphorus and potassium

One of the major aims of organic farming is to minimise the use of non-renewable resources. It follows, therefore, that soil nutrient status must be maintained as far as possible through management means and by efficient nutrient cycling within the farm, rather than relying on imported mineral fertiliser. In grassland, the main priority concerns the removal of nutrients from fields cut for hay or silage. With a yield of 10 t DM/ha/annum, nutrient offtake in the herbage will be in the region of 80 kg P_2O_5/ha/annum and 260 kg K_2O/ha/annum (Fowler *et al.*, 1993; Younie *et al.*, 1998). This can obviously have a major effect on soil K and P content and consequently on herbage and crop yield.

Figure 6.3 shows the adverse effect which high yields of first cut silage can have on exchangeable soil K content in just one season, in grass-white clover swards in an organic crop rotations trial on a sandy loam soil in NE Scotland (10% clay). The relationship is significant at the P<0.001 level.

Figure 6.3 **Effect of first cut silage yield in previous season on soil K status on a sandy loam soil in NE Scotland** (from Younie and Baars, 1997).

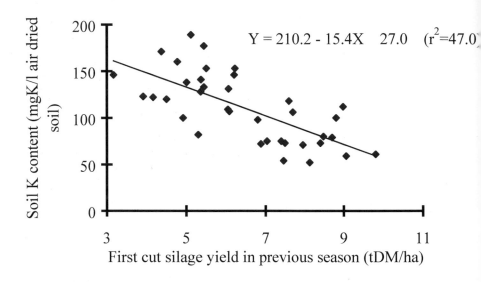

Similarly, on a sandy soil in the Netherlands, Younie and Baars (1997) reported reductions of 62% and 39% in soil K content over three years in, respectively, cut and cut/grazed organic grass/clover leys yielding 9 to 11 t DM/ha. In contrast, on similarly managed swards on clay soils, no decline in soil K content was detected. Clovers are poor competitors for soil P and K compared to grass. The reductions in K content in the experiments of Baars described above caused a significant loss of clover from the swards. This adverse effect of low soil K content on clover content will restrict the input of atmospherically fixed N in the system and have a knock-on effect on herbage yield.

Manurial strategy

The manurial strategy needs to have a combination of rotational and annual approaches. It is important to have a long-term or rotational perspective since the farmer relies, to a large extent, on release of N, P and K from soil reserves. Changes in soil nutrient status should be monitored regularly, therefore; say every 3 to 4 years. Lime is permitted if pH falls to undesirable levels. Deficiencies in soil P and K can be met from imports of approved, composted or aerated non-organic manures or from approved mineral fertilisers. Rock phosphate can be used to overcome P deficiency, but is not immediately effective so the farmer must anticipate requirements 2 to 3 years in advance. Approval for use of mineral potassium sources (e.g. potassium sulphate or sylvinite) must be sought before use.

On an annual basis, it is essential that manure storage facilities are effective, so that nutrient losses from the system can be minimised. Organic grass-clover swards intended for conservation must be given the highest priority in the distribution of manures, particularly on sandy soils. A separate application of manure should be applied for each cut, starting in late January/February for the first cut. Ideally, management of any one field should **alternate annually between cutting and grazing** rather than continuous cutting, in order to minimise nutrient offtake. In contrast, no manure application is necessary for grass for grazing. In practice, application rates of farmyard manure (FYM) or slurry will be determined by the quantity available, but a possible annual manurial strategy could be as follows:

	Source	of:	Application rates	
	N	P, K	1st cut	2nd, 3rd cuts
Grazing	Clover, Soil N	Recycled, Soil P, K	N/A	N/A
Cutting	Clover, Soil N	FYM, slurry, Soil P, K	FYM: 20t/ha, or Slurry: 22,500 l/ha	FYM: 20t/ha or Slurry: 22,500 l/ha

POTENTIAL LEVELS OF HERBAGE YIELD AND LIVESTOCK OUTPUT

Satisfactory annual yields and first cut silage yields are obtainable in clover-based organic systems provided a good legume content in the sward can be maintained and assuming satisfactory levels of soil P, K and pH status and soil moisture supply (Table 6.4).

The herbage yields shown in Table 6.4 generally reflect the conditions under which the swards were monitored, namely site quality, legume species, cutting date or regrowth interval. For example, the first cut silage yields of 4 to 5tDM/ha (**mean 4.5 t DM/ha**) were from cuts taken in mid-May, whilst the yields of 5 to 6 tDM/ha (**mean 5.6 t DM/ha**) were from cuts taken in mid-June. The mean annual yield from swards which were mainly cut was **10.8 t DM/ha**.

Spring growth in an unfertilised clover sward is lower than in a fertilised sward. In the systems comparison reported by Younie and Wightman (1992), mean herbage biomass in the organic sward at turnout in early May was 738 kgDM/ha, almost exactly half that of the fertilised control. Where spring growth is particularly important, e.g. with lambing ewes, it is vital that planning for spring grazing begins in the previous autumn. The

Table6. 4 Reported levels of herbage production from organic grassland

Reference	Sward type	Annual (grazing)	Annual (mainly cut)	1st cut silage	Stocking rate (LU[5] per forage ha)
Baars & Veltman (i) (2000)	G/WC[1]/RC[2]		12.6	4.5	
Baars & Veltman (ii) (2000)	G/WC/RC		12.3	4.7	
Baars (2000)	G/WC		10.5		
Fowler et al. (1993)	G/WC[1]	10.1	10.1		1.6
Halberg & Kristensen (1997)	Varied	8.2/7.0[6]			1.6
Houghton & Poole (1990)	Unspecified				1.6
Jones et al. (i) (1996)	G/WC	7.2		4.2	1.7
Jones et al. (ii) (1996)	G/WC	7.1	8.8		1.6
Jones et al. (iii) (1996)	G/RC[2]		14		
Lampkin & Measures (1999)	Unspecified				1.7
Newton & Stopes (1995)	G/WC		13.0[4]		
Philipps (2000)	G/WC		12.5[4]		
Redman (1991)	Unspecified				1.8
Van d. Meer & B. Hofmann (1989)	G/WC	6.4			
Van d. Meer & B. Hofmann (1989)	G/RC, L[3]		10.9		1.9
Younie & Wightman (1992)	G/WC	8.7	8.9	5.9	2.1
Younie (1997)	G/WC		7.6	5.4	1.2
Younie et al. (1996)	G/WC		8.0	5.5	

[1] Grass-white clover,   [2] Grass-red clover,   [3] Lucerne,   [4] Cut to ground level   [6] Calculated as SFU * 1.35.
[5] LU: One Livestock Unit = One Freisian cow producing 6000 litres per annum

sward should be grazed down hard in November/December to encourage clover content, but stock should be removed no later than late December, and no further winter grazing should take place until turnout in spring.

The mean of the stocking rates in Table 6.4 is **1.68 livestock units per forage hectare**. These figures take account of the grass required for winter keep. Where the soil type is satisfactory and clover content is high enough, a stocking rate of 1.6 LU/ha/annum is feasible in practice. This will be more than adequate for most UK farmers, given that many will be aiming for a stocking rate below this level, in order to claim Extensification Scheme subsidy payment.

REFERENCES

Baars, T. (2000) Effective use of manure and fertiliser in organically grown grass/clover swards. In Soegaard K., Ohlsson C., Sehested J., Hutchings N. J., Kristensen T., (eds.) *Grassland Farming: Balancing environmental and economic demands,* Proc. 18th General Meeting of European Grassland Federation, 524-526.

Baars, T. & Veltman, L. (2000) Adapted grass/clover mixtures for ley farming - a participatory approach to develop organic farming systems. In Soegaard K., Ohlsson C., Sehested J., Hutchings N. J., Kristensen T., (eds.) *Grassland Farming: Balancing environmental and economic demands,* Proc. 18th General Meeting of European Grassland Federation, 542-544.

Courtney A.D. (1985) Impact and control of docks in grassland. In Brockman J.S. (ed) *Weeds, Pests and Diseases of Grassland and Herbage Legumes.* Occasional Symposium

No. 18, British Grassland Society; British Crop Protection Council Monograph No. 29, 120-127.

Davies D.A. & Hopkins A. (1996) Production benefits of legumes in grassland. In Younie D. (ed) *Legumes in Sustainable Farming Systems*, Occasional Symposium, No. 30, British Grassland Society, Reading, 234-246.

Foster L. (1988). Herbs in pastures. Development and research in Britain, 1850-1984. *Biological Agriculture and Horticulture*, **5**, 97-133.

Fowler S. M., Watson C. A. & Wilman D (1993). N, P and K on organic farms: herbage and cereal production, purchases and sales. *Journal of Agricultural Science*, Cambridge, **120**, 353-360.

Halberg N. and Kristensen, I.S. (1997). Expected Crop Yield Loss When Converting to Organic Dairy Farming in Denmark. Biological Agriculture and Horticulture, 1997, Vol. 14, pp. 25-41.

Hansen, S. (1995) Effects of manure treatment and soil compaction on plant production of a dairy farm system converting to organic farming practice. *Agriculture, Ecosystems and Environment*, **56** (3), 173-186.

Hopkins A., Jones E.L, Bowling P.J., & Johnson R.H. (1997) Cultural methods of dock control in permanent pasture. *Fifth Research Conference, British Grassland Society*, September 1997, 39-40.

Houghton M. & Poole A.H. (1990) *Organic Milk Production.* Genus Information Unit Report No. 70, 31pp.

Jones E.L., Bowling P.J. & Haggar R.J. (1996) Forage yields and quality during conversion. In: Haggar R.J. & Padel S. (eds) *Conversion to Organic Milk Production.* Institute of Grassland and Environmental Research Technical Review No. 4, 57-65.

Kristensen E.S., Høgh-Jensen H. & Kristensen I.S. (1995). A simple model for estimation of atmospherically-derived nitrogen in grass-clover systems. *Biological Agriculture and Horticulture*, 12, 263-276.

Laidlaw, A.S., Teuber, N.G. & Withers, J.A. (1992) Out-of-season management of grass/clover swards to manipulate clover content. *Grass and Forage Science*, 47, 220-229.

Lampkin, N. and Measures, M. (1999) *Organic Farm Management Handbook, 3rd Edition*. University of Wales, Aberystwyth and Elm Farm Research Centre, 163pp.

Moloney S.C. and Milne G.D. (1993). Establishment and management of Grasslands Puna chicory used as a specialist, high quality forage herb. *Proceedings of the New Zealand Grassland Association*, **55**, 113-118.

Newton J & Stopes C (1995). Grassland productivity on organic farms, 1992-1994. *Elm Farm Research Centre Bulletin*, No. 18, 2-6.

Philipps, L. (2000) Achievable levels of production for organic grassland. In Soegaard K., Ohlsson C., Sehested J., Hutchings N. J., Kristensen T., (eds.) *Grassland Farming: Balancing environmental and economic demands*, Proc. 18th General Meeting of European Grassland Federation, 548-551.

Redman M. (1991) Organic dairy costings: Update. *New Farmer and Grower*, **33**, 20-21

Swift G., Davies D.H.K., Tiley G.E.D. & Younie D (1990) The nutritive value of broad-leaved weeds and forage herbs in grassland. *Scottish Agricultural College, Technical Note No.223.*

Umrani A.P. (1998) *Sustainable approaches for rangeland management and livestock production in Pakistan.* PhD Thesis, University of Aberdeen.

Van der Meer H.G. & Baan Hofman T. (1989). Contribution of legumes to yield and nitrogen economy of leys on a biodynamic farm. In Plancquaert P. & Haggar R.J. (eds) *Legumes in Farming Systems*, Developments in Plant and Soil Science, **37**, 25-36.

Van Eekeren, N. (2000) Balancing summer rations of dairy cows by means of urea content in bulk tank milk. In Soegaard K., Ohlsson C., Sehested J., Hutchings N. J., Kristensen T., (eds.) *Grassland Farming: Balancing environmental and economic demands*, Proc. 18th General Meeting of European Grassland Federation, 555-557.

Welsh J.P. (1995) Dock control demonstration trial. *Elm Farm Research Centre Bulletin*, 18, 6-7.

Whitehead, D.C. (1995). *Grassland Nitrogen.* CAB International, Wallingford, 397pp.

Wilman D. & Derrick R.W. (1994) Concentration and availability to sheep of N, P, K, Ca, Mg and Na in chickweed, dandelion, dock, ribwort and spurrey, compared with perennial ryegrass. *Journal of Agricultural Science, Cambridge*, **122**, 217-223.

Younie D. (1992). Potential output from forage legumes in organic systems. In Peeters A & Van Bol V. (eds) *Potential and limits of organic farming*, Proceedings of an EC Workshop, Louvain-la-Neuve, Belgium, September 1992, 116-129.

Younie D. (1997) Organic Beef and Sheep Systems. Paper presented at 'Grass is Greener' *British Grassland Society Winter Meeting 1997.* Great Malvern, November 1997.

Younie D. & Baars T. (1997). Resource Use in Organic Grassland: The Central Bank and the Art Gallery of Organic Farming. In Isart J. & Llerena J. (eds) *Resource Use in Organic Farming,* Proceedings of Third Workshop

101

of European Network for Scientific Co-ordination in Organic Farming (ENOF), University of Ancona, Italy, 43-60.

Younie, D. and Giordano, A. (1993).Pattern of crop development in fertilised and unfertilised grass/clover swards grown for silage. *White Clover in Europe: State of the Art*, FAO REUR Series 29 (Ed J. Frame), 63-65.

Younie D. & Wightman P.S. (1992) Herbage production over eight years from clover-based and intensively fertilised swards under grazing and silage management. *Proc. Third Research Meeting, British Grassland Society*, Sept. 1992.

Younie D., Watson, C.A. & Squire, G. (1996). A comparison of crop rotations in organic farming: agronomic performance. In Clarke J.H., Davies D.H.K., Dampney P.M.R., Froud-Williams R.J., Griffith P.J., Lane A., Sim L. & Stevens D.B. (eds) *Rotations and Cropping Systems.* Aspects of Applied Biology, 47, AAB, 379-382

Younie, D., Wilson, J.F., Carr, G. & Watt, C.W. (1984) The effect of undersowing, nitrogen application and date of sowing on white clover establishment. In Thomson, D.J. (ed.) *Forage Legumes*, Occasional Symposium No. 16, British Grassland Society, Reading, 182-183.

Younie, D., Umrani, A.P., Gray, D. and Coutts, M. (1997). Influence of chicory or ryegrass diets on trace element status of lambs. RASE Conference: '*Organic Farming - Science into Practice*'. RASE, NAC, Stoneleigh, November 1997.

Younie D., Wilson J.F., Reid C. & Wightman, P.S. (1998). Maintenance of soil potassium in organic farming silage systems. In Nagy G. & Peto K (eds.) *Ecology and Grassland*, 17th General Meeting of European Grassland Federation, Debrecen, Hungary, 289-292.

Chapter 7

Organic Milk Production on Two Contrasting Dairy Farms

J. NEWMAN[1] and R. F. WELLER[2]
[1]*Abbey Home Farm, Cirencester, Gloucestershire, GL7 5HA*
[2]*Institute for Grassland and Environmental Research,*
Trawsgoed, Aberystwyth, Ceredigion, SY23 4LL

INTRODUCTION

In this paper the management practices and performance of two contrasting organic dairy farms are discussed:

Case study 1: Abbey Home Farm, Gloucestershire - a **mixed ley/arable** commercial dairy farm in a relatively low rainfall area.

Case study 2: Ty Gwyn Farm, Ceredigion, Wales – a **mainly grassland** organic dairy farm in west Wales established as a research and demonstration farm.

STANDARDS FOR ORGANIC DAIRY PRODUCTION

In addition to the standards for crop and grassland production, the key standards relating to organic dairy production are:

1. At least 60% of the dry matter intake of the dairy cow must come from a fully organic source. Up to 24th August 2005 it is permitted to make use of a 10%

maximum annual allowance of permitted conventional feedstuffs, with a daily maximum intake of 25%, on a dry matter basis.
2. The use of routine prophylactic drugs is prohibited, e.g. dry cow therapy.
3. At least 60% of the annual dry matter intake must come from the farm.
4. At least 60% of the dry matter intake must be from forage, on a daily basis.

It should be noted that the use of antibiotics is not prohibited and animal welfare is of prime importance. However withdrawal periods are longer than in conventional production, typically three times the conventional withdrawal period, up to a maximum of 56 days.

CASE STUDY 1: ABBEY HOME FARM

The farm is located on Cotswold brash soil and has an annual rainfall of 700mm. Conversion to organic production commenced in 1991 and the farm has been selling organic milk since 1994. It is a mixed farm with 250 hectares cereals and beans, and 320 hectares grassland, supporting dairy, beef and sheep enterprises. It also has pig, poultry and vegetable enterprises to supply the farm shop. The dairy unit comprises 150 cows.

As well as the day-to-day detail and challenges presented by managing the Abbey Home Farm unit it is important to realize the dairy's contribution to the farm's sustainability, both financially and organically. The dairy is the biggest financial contributor to the turnover of the Abbey Home Farm business.

Equally important, the dairy allows fertility-building legume crops to be utilized effectively, provides a valuable manure source and drives the farm's cropping rotation.

Dairy breeds

At Abbey Home Farm the breeding policy is to retain the Friesian type of Holstein/Friesian as this animal seems to suit the organic system and aids with beef calf production. The size of the animals within the herd is being increased, hopefully to increase potential forage intakes. Artificial insemination is permitted. The use of sexed semen is still under review by the Soil Association and may well be permitted.

Crop production and feeding management

Forage provides 60 to 95% of the annual feed requirements for the organic dairy herd. Good forage management from production through to feeding is essential to meet the cow's nutritional requirements and to achieve optimum milk yields and good milk quality. Clearly the emphasis is on the production of milk from forage. This requires the production of high quality forage, ideally at a reasonably high protein level to reduce the requirement for bought in feeds. Home-grown cereals provide good energy sources. Red and white clover ley mixtures are a central feature of organic dairy systems in the UK. They are grown for their ability to fix nitrogen and therefore build up soil fertility, but they also produce highly digestible pastures and high quality conserved forages with high proteins. A red clover ley can fix up to 250 kg N/ha/annum.

The white clover leys are used predominately for grazing. The leys can be slower to grow in the spring but this is usually compensated by an extended growing season in the autumn.

105

Clover pastures maintain their quality even when in flower. The protein content of the grazing swards increases throughout the grazing season to levels in excess of the cow's requirement. Therefore, if a concentrate supplement is to be fed a high energy, low protein feed (e.g. cereal grains) is offered to increase the energy: protein ratio of the diet and improve the utilisation of protein by the cow.

High levels of white clover in the grazing swards do not inherently mean bloat. Buffer feeding is important to reduce the risk and at Abbey Home Farm good quality hay or big bale silage is available throughout the grazing season. The only cases of bloat on the farm have been related to problems with management such as holding back cows without access to buffer feed and then the cows feeding rapidly on low dry matter, clover-rich swards. Young stock brought up with clover leys seem to be able to deal with the clover levels better and we have had no case of bloat in these groups during rearing and then when in milk. Avoiding daily fluctuations in the quantity of herbage available for grazing will minimise the risk of bloat. Experience in New Zealand has suggested that there is an increased risk of bloat due to 'grazing pressure' when a large number of cows are grazed in one group.

Experiments at Abbey Home Farm with herbs in ley mixtures have shown benefits from the inclusion of chicory, trefoil and plantain. There does seem to be an improvement in animal health and general well-being. As yet we do not have sufficient experience of yield from these herbal leys to see if they could be substituted for the ryegrass/clover mix. There may also be benefits from including other grass species into seed mixtures.

Making high quality silage from red clover and lucerne leys can be challenging but the results can also be impressive.

Silage with protein and energy concentrations of 18% and 11.5 MJ ME/kg DM, respectively, is perfectly possible. Most organic farms have reported few problems when ensiling grass/legume herbage, with good fermentation and low ammonia-N contents. Wilting is essential and at Abbey Home Farm the aim is to reach a dry matter content of 25% to 30%, which may involve wilting for 24 to 36 hours. However, it is important to avoid over-wilting grass/legume crops, including excessive turning of the cut swaths, since field losses will increase due to leaf shatter in the legumes, leading to lower silage quality.

Having a mixture of grasses in the ley with the legumes is important to increase the concentration of readily-fermentable sugar to improve the quality of the silage fermentation. At Abbey Home Farm an inoculant is used to aid fermentation along with short chopping. It is important to pay great attention to detail in clamp management, rolling well and then sheeting and applying weight to the sheet as soon as possible after the cut is completed. This is essential to avoid poor fermentation, high dry matter losses within the clamp and spoilage on the top and sides of the clamp.

Inevitably, silage dry matter yields have been lower compared with those from fertilised ryegrass swards and this, combined with the fact that legumes have increased intake, can put pressure on the total area required for forage production and therefore on stocking rates. To avoid any potential shortages of forage at Abbey Home Farm, an area is sown to arable silage or whole-crop cereal, often undersown with a clover ley. This proves a very good way of establishing a ley and at the same time produces an alternative forage. Of course it also provides an opportunity to claim arable area payments to help pay for the reseeding of the ley.

Diets for the organic dairy herd are based on high quantities of forage, and maintaining a reserve stock of silage or hay is a good insurance against either dry summers or long winters. Since grass conservation leads to the substantial removal of nutrients from the soil, the fields at Abbey Home Farm receive at least 25 tonnes/hectare of composted manure per season, spread initially in March and occasionally between first and second cuts of silage.

Having produced this high quality forage element in the cows diet, it then becomes easier to balance the diet with home-grown cereals and pulses. The requirement for bought in concentrate is thus reduced. The herd at Abbey Home Farm is divided into two or three groups based on milk yield and days since calving. The aim is to feed a small quantity of a relatively high protein, genetically-modified (GM)-free, concentrate such as rapeseed meal, for the first 100 days of lactation, with a target of achieving a crude protein level in the diet of 16 to 17 % of the total DM. All bought-in concentrate must be approved i.e. GM-free and not chemically-extracted. Currently 955 kg of concentrate is fed per cow per annum. The diet is fed as a complete diet through a mixer wagon. There is access to rock salt *ad libitum*, and seaweed meal is added to the ration every other day at a rate of 25 kg per group.

Milk yields per lactation average 5950 litres per cow and 5157 litres per heifer. The overall herd average yield is 5700 litres.

Animal health and welfare

The challenge of running a dairy unit without the routine use of antibiotics can seem daunting. Drying off cows without dry cow therapy, treating mastitis with homeopathy and using herbs to stimulate oestrus can require large leaps of faith, but as with many things, once a few successes have been achieved confidence levels rise. Attention to detail is vital and we believe in the old adage that prevention is easier than cure. There must be time allowed for stock to be observed and hygiene, ventilation, and proper handling are important if disease is to be kept to a minimum.

The farm uses various homeopathic nosodes in the water troughs to keep cell counts down, reduce the incidence of mastitis and ease calvings. The rolling cell count is 233,000 cells/ml, incidence of clinical mastitis is 14% and there are very few cases of milk fever or assisted calvings. A close eye is kept on fertility and cows not seen bulling are given a veterinary examination and may receive an ovary massage to stimulate oestrus. Tail paint is also used to improve oestrous detection. Considerable time and money has been spent on improving the dairy buildings, yards and milking equipment.

The walls of the milking parlour have been lined with plastic to allow easy cleaning, entry and exit routes have been improved and new equipment installed recently includes electronic mastitis detection. The parlour is serviced every 800 hours and regular dynamic milking tests are carried out. This is all about trying to make milking a fast, stress-free and painless operation for both cows and herdsman. Each day yards are bedded down with fresh straw and the standings scraped daily. Both the milking and dry cow yards are cleaned out every six weeks to avoid build up of bacteria.

Although there are regular veterinary visits for fertility massages and pregnancy diagnosis, the vet bill is currently £29 per cow per annum. Other organic farms have also reported lower vet bills following the change from conventional to organic farming. At Abbey Home Farm problems such as ketosis and laminitis, often associated with high concentrate diets, are rare. At the end of lactation cows are dried off within a period of 2 to 3 days, a teat sealant applied and the udders closely inspected during the following two weeks. To ensure good health is maintained from birth, calves are now reared on nurse cows (either dairy cows or beef x dairy crossbreds). Good stockmanship and the early detection of illness are key factors in the maintenance of good herd health.

Herd performance

During conversion, stocking rates will fall whilst a legume-based grassland system is established and grassland productivity falls temporarily. On many farms the stocking rate will fall by 10 to 20% during the conversion period. However, the magnitude of the change will depend on how intensive the system was prior to conversion and also on the clover content of the swards at the start of the conversion period. During the conversion period the availability of on-farm manure sources will be limited – any low soil P and K indices are better corrected prior to the start of the conversion to organic farming. Following the establishment of the rotation, an increase in crop production is likely as the rotation starts to work and, as experience is gained in managing clover leys, the stocking rate can increase. Currently Abbey Home Farm has a stocking rate of 1.6 cows per hectare. Yields on the farm remained fairly static through conversion and have since increased. Milk from forage has also risen. Concentrate costs are high with rolled organic cereal coming in at £186 per tonne, but a good milk price of 29.5p per litre still leads to a respectable margin over concentrates. Organic milk production is both challenging and rewarding as the results illustrate (Table 7.1).

Table 7.1   Abbey Home Farm Dairy Gross Margin, 2000.

Stocking rate	1.6 cows/ha		
Concentrate use	0.19kg/litre		
Replacement rate	20%		
Milk price	29.5p/litre		
Output		£/cow	p/litre
Milk sales	5700 litres @ 29.5p/litre	1682	
Calves	0.9 calves/cow @ £37.50	34	
Culls	18% @ £300/head	54	
Replacements	20% @ £650/head	-130	
Total output		1639	28.75
Variable costs			
Concentrates	955kg/cow @ £172/t	164	
Vet. & med.		29	
A.I. & recording		42	
Other		40	
Total		275	
Margin over purchased feed		1475	25.87
Gross margin excluding forage costs		1364	23.93
		Per cow	Per ha.
Forage costs (£)		28	45
Milk from forage (l)		3399	5439
Gross margin including forage costs (£)		1336	2137

CASE STUDY 2: TY GWYN FARM

This 94.5 ha dairy farm is situated in West Wales and has an annual rainfall of 1,200 mm. Ty Gwyn is a research and demonstration farm within the Institute of Grassland and Environmental Research (IGER), conducting trials to evaluate factors affecting the performance of organic dairy production systems. The farm was converted from an intensive system based on an annual input of 380 kg of fertiliser N/ha to an organic system using N-fixation from both red and white clover as the main source of nitrogen for crop production. With the exception of lime, which is applied when fields are re-seeded, no non-organic fertilisers have been applied since 1991. N-fixation by clover and the on-farm slurry and solid manure provide the main nutrients required for crop production.

Until 1998, all concentrate feeds were purchased, providing an extra input of N, P and K into the farm nutrient cycle and balancing those exported from the farm as milk and meat. From 1992 to 1998 all crops were either grazed or conserved as forage, with grain production starting in 1999. The farm was converted during the 1992-94 period and managed as a single dairy unit until September 1998. From 1999 onwards the farm has been divided into two separate organic dairy production systems.

Performance of the farm 1992-1998

Forage production

A crop rotation was established on 75% of the total land area with 25% maintained as permanent pasture. The main objectives of the rotation were to provide a balance between N-fixing and N-demanding crops, build-up and maintain soil fertility, minimise weed problems and provide sufficient forage for both grazing and ensiling. The crop rotation was:

Year 1:	Arable silage conserved from spring barley undersown with a mixture of Italian ryegrass and red clover.
Years 2 to 3:	Three cuts/year of Italian ryegrass/red clover, followed by autumn grazing with cows and tack sheep.
Year 4:	Cereals for arable silage.
Years 5 to 9:	Perennial ryegrass/white clover mixtures for grazing and first-cut silage.

Spring barley provided a good cover crop for the establishment of Italian ryegrass swards and also prevented docks becoming a problem in the re-seeded swards.

Table 7.2   Forage yields at Ty Gwyn

Year	Management system	Annual forage production (t DM/ha)	Stocking rate (LSU[1]/ha)
1991	Conventional	10.50	1.97
1992-4	In-conversion	8.31	1.55
1995	Organic Year 1	8.37	1.49
1996	Organic Year 2	9.49	1.76
1997	Organic Year 3	10.03	1.84
1998	Organic Year 4	9.15	1.70

[1] LSU = Livestock Unit.

At the start of the conversion period many of the fields had a white clover content of less than 5%, resulting in low N-fixation. As shown in Table 7.2, converting the farm from an intensive system based on 380 kg of N/ha to an organic system in the minimum 2-year period led to a reduction in both crop yields and the stocking rate during the conversion period. However, following the establishment of the crop rotation, both forage yields and the stocking rate increased, with the mixed Italian ryegrass/red clover swards ultimately contributing over 60% of the total forage conserved as silage.

To meet the requirements for high-forage diets during the winter housing period from October to the end of April, 2.5 to 3.0 t DM of silage/cow was required for the dairy herd. The high yields and stocking rates achieved in 1997 (Table 7.2) were the result of a very good growing season and the yields recorded in 1998 are nearer to the yields and stocking rates that can be sustained over a period of years.

As the organic system is based on high-forage diets it is essential to maintain a reserve stock of forage for feeding during periods of shortage. The DM yields produced by the Italian ryegrass/red clover swards ranged from 9 to 14 tonnes DM/hectare, with 8 to 11 tonnes DM/ha. from the re-seeded perennial ryegrass/white clover swards and 7 to 10 tonnes DM/ha from the permanent pastures. Slurry was applied for both first and second silage cuts and the grazing swards were injected with slurry in early summer. The solid manure was applied to the permanent pastures prior to the start of the grazing season.

All ensiled crops were ensiled with a *Lactobacillus plantarum* inoculant to ensure good fermentation and analysis of the silage samples showed that the majority of silages were within the following range:

Crude protein: 13 to 20% of DM
Metabolisable energy: 10.3 to 11.4 MJ/kg DM
Ammonia-N: < 5% of total N.

The results have also shown only small differences in quality between the Italian ryegrass/red clover and perennial ryegrass/white clover silage samples.

Grazing strategy

The balance between the areas allocated for grazing and conservation is critical to meet both the demands of the herd for forage during the grazing season and ensuring sufficient forage is ensiled for the winter period. Experience at Ty Gwyn has shown that the objective of maintaining a conservation: grazing ratio of 2:1, 1:1 and 1:2 during the spring, early summer and late summer periods provided the correct balance in most seasons. However, in some years late spring growth or relatively dry summer periods either decreased the quantities of forage available for conservation or led to increased grazing pressure.

The grazing policy for the Ty Gwyn dairy herd has been to maintain the swards at a minimum grazing height of 6 to 8 cm (excluding rejected areas) during the grazing season. The average white clover content of the swards (DM basis) ranged from 15 to 25% in May, increasing to between 40 to 50% in July and August, then declining to 20 to 30% in October. To reduce the clover content in swards where the white clover has become too dominant, either a silage cut was taken, rather than the sward being grazed, or grass seed slot-seeded into the existing sward. Slot-seeding either Italian or Westerwolds ryegrass into an existing sward during the previous autumn improved spring growth and led to a 10 to 14 day earlier turn-out date. Heavy grazing of clover-based swards should be avoided as the results from Ty Gwyn show this reduced both the clover content and total yield in the following year (Weller and Cooper, 1995).

Herbs have been included in the perennial ryegrass/white clover swards at Ty Gwyn to increase the diversity of plant species in the sward and also to increase the mineral content of the swards. However, there have been large differences recorded between species in relation to their establishment and persistency. Suppressing docks in grazing swards is also important, and the establishment and maintenance of dense swards that include both erect and prostrate varieties of perennial ryegrass in the seed mixtures prevented docks increasing in the grazing swards. The swards have also been regularly topped during the grazing season. In late October or early November, when the cows are housed for the winter period, sheep have been allowed to graze off the surplus herbage. The sheep were removed at the end of December to ensure spring growth for the dairy herd was not restricted due to over grazing by the sheep.

Feeding

Throughout the year concentrates were fed to yield and cows producing either more than 15 litres of milk/day from winter silage-based diets or over 20 litres during the grazing season received concentrates. The concentrate feeds have been a blend of an organic cereal grain (barley, oats or wheat) and an acceptable protein supplement, including organic field beans and GM-free expelled soya beans. To avoid post-calving and infertility problems that can occur when there is a mineral deficiency, seaweed meal and coarse rock salt have been offered to the cows since the start of the conversion period.

Clover silages are very palatable with high intake characteristics. In a feeding trial at IGER (Weller *et al.*, 1996b) cows in early lactation were individually fed and offered 6.5 kg of concentrates/day and access to first cut Italian ryegrass/red clover silage *ad libitum*. Total DM intake was 18.9 kg/day, silage DM intake 12.4 kg/day and average milk yield 37 litres/cow.

Performance

During the conversion period total milk production/ha declined, with yields increasing to the pre-conversion level by the third year of full organic production (Table 7.3). Yields/cow increased following conversion with the fat and protein contents of the milk also increasing from 3.94 and 3.17% to 4.17 and 3.34%, respectively. The milk yields recorded at Ty Gwyn are similar to those recorded in other herds converting during the same period (Weller *et al.*, 1996a). As a primarily spring-calving herd the major portion (62 to 65%) of the total milk was produced during the grazing season. On the majority of dairy farms the level of concentrate fed per cow declines following conversion, leading to an increase in the production of milk from forage. In Year 3 of full organic production the margin over purchased feed increased due to an increase in the premium paid for the organic milk.

The level of milk production from forage is an important factor on all dairy farms and critical to the performance of organic systems. Utilised Metabolisable Energy output per hectare (UME, GJ/ha) is a useful method of estimating the efficiency of forage utilisation for the individual dairy herd, with the values increasing as home-grown forage provides a higher proportion of the energy requirements for the herd. The UME values were calculated to measure the changes in forage utilisation of the Ty Gwyn herd. Prior to conversion the UME output was 75.5 GJ/ha, declining during conversion to 52.2 GJ/ha. In the first year post-conversion the UME output increased to 55.3 GJ/ha and in Year 3 of full organic production, following an increase in forage production, stocking rates and total milk production, the UME output increased to 76.7 GJ/ha.

Table 7.3   Performance of the Ty Gwyn dairy herd

| | **Year** | | |
	1991	**1992 to 1994**	**1995 to 1997**
	Conventional	Conversion	Organic Year 1 to Year 3
Total annual milk production (litres/ha)	10,080	7737	8604 to 10,073
Annual rolling average yield (litres/cow)	4890	5146	5496 to 5755
Average lactation yields (litres/cow)	5494	5663	6132 to 6105
Concentrates (t/cow)	1.1	1.4	1.5 to 1.2
Margin over purchased feed			
£/cow	853	850	828 to 1012
p/litre	16.98	17.91	17.16 to 20.8

Health and fertility

As shown in Table 7.4, no major health problems were recorded at Ty Gwyn and the results are similar to those recorded on other organic farms during both the conversion period (Weller and Cooper, 1996) and full organic production (Weller and Bowling, 2000).

Table 7. 4   Health and fertility of the Ty Gwyn herd

Cases/100 cows	Conversion	Year 1	Organic Year 2	Year 3
Clinical mastitis	21.8	11.0	18.9	15.9
Lameness	12.0	9.6	10.1	12.5
Milk fever	5.3	4.1	10.1	1.1
Ketosis/digestive upsets	2.7	1.4	0.3	0
Bloat	0.4	0	0.1	0
Hypomagnesaemia	0	0	0	0
Retained foetal membranes	3.5	5.5	5.0	6.8
Vulval discharge/metritis	16.6	42.5	21.4	33.0
Fertility problems	14.6	15.1	49.1	5.7
Abortions	0.5	1.4	0	1.1
Culling %	17.3	37.0	15.6	26.4
Somatic cell count ('000 cells/ml)	271	262	232	245

The incidence of clinical mastitis at Ty Gwyn was lower than comparable conventional herds. Mild cases of mastitis were treated with alternative remedies, including udder linaments and phytolacca, with antibiotics only used for the more severe cases.

In some organic herds there is a higher incidence of mastitis during the dry period than would be expected on a conventional farm where long-acting antibiotics are used during the dry period. A study of the level of somatic cell counts in the milk from individual cows (Weller and Davies, 1998) showed that both during lactation and between parities the counts were higher than those normally recorded in conventional herds. The incidence of lameness was low reflecting the high forage and lower protein content of the diets, the feeding of higher DM silages, the standard of the winter housing facilities and the condition of the stone tracks used during the grazing season.

The incidence of metabolic disorders, including milk fever and bloat, was low and similar to the levels recorded on other organic dairy farms. The low incidence of bloat is attributed to the continuous grazing system that avoided large variations in the quantity of herbage available to the herd each day. Although the number of fertility problems was high in Year 1 of full organic production, overall the number of problems was lower than those recorded in conventional dairy herds. The overall culling rate was similar to conventional herds but higher than those recorded in many organic dairy herds, with infertility the main reason for culling cows from the herd. No parasitic problems were recorded in the dairy herd and generally, with the exception of an outbreak of coccidiosis, few health problems occurred with the young cattle.

The policy for the reproductive management of the herd was to inseminate the majority of cows and only use a sweeper bull for cows not conceiving after three inseminations. No major reproductive problems were recorded in the herd and the pregnancy rate was within the targets set for the herd. The number of days from calving to conception was slightly higher, and the overall pregnancy rate to first service of 50 to 60% was lower, than the targets set for the herd (Table 7.5).

Table 7.5 Reproductive performance of the Ty Gwyn herd

	Conversion	Organic		
		Year 1	Year 2	Year 3
Services/pregnancy (Target: <2.0)	2.10	1.74	1.59	2.37
Days to conception (Target: 90 to 95)	97.3	94.3	120.5	84.7
Conception to first service (%) (Target: 50 to 60%)	42.0	57.4	46.4	40.7
Overall pregnancy rate (%) (Target 85 to 90%)	86.0	90.2	87.0	86.8

Summary of the results from Ty Gwyn farm during the 1992-98 period

During both the conversion period and the following three years of full organic production the clover content in the sward and level of forage production influenced the performance of the farm. The decline in forage yields at Ty Gwyn during the conversion period was greater than for those farms where either the conversion period was longer or the N-fertiliser input pre-conversion was lower. Following the establishment of the crop rotation the stocking density increased above the target figure of 1.7 LSU/ha. As shown in Table 7.2 the stocking rate increased to 1.84 LSU/ha in 1997, attributable to a very good growing season and ample forage for both grazing and conservation. However, managing the farm at this high stocking rate would not be sustainable over a period of years as shown by the yields recorded in 1998 when the stocking rate was 1.7 LSU/ha. Reducing the stocking rate to below 1.7 LSU/ha would increase the quantity of forage available per cow for both grazing and conservation, reduce the concentrate inputs and increase the level of milk production per cow. However, on most farms reducing the stocking rate would reduce milk production and income/ha.

No major health and fertility problems were recorded in the Ty Gwyn herd during the 1992-98 period. The number of cases of clinical mastitis was low when compared with the levels recorded in conventional herds However, for some organic herds the withdrawal of long-acting antibiotics at the end of lactation has increased the number of cases of mastitis during the dry period. High cell counts reduce the quality of milk for processing and can also significantly reduce milk yield during lactation (Hovi, 1997). The relatively low incidence of bloat at Ty Gwyn (Table 7.4) was similar to the levels recorded on other organic and low-input farms where clover-based swards are grazed throughout the growing season. The incidence of bloat reported is significantly lower when compared with the problems reported in New Zealand herds.

Purchased organic feeds are expensive in relation to home-grown forage and as organic dairy production is based on high-forage diets the priority has been to produce sufficient quantities of forage, not only for grazing and conservation. There may also be benefits from introducing additional forage crops, including forage maize or fodder beet, into the existing rotation (Weller, 1999) as both crops provide the readily available energy that is required by the dairy cow in early lactation. However, a balance needs to be made between the benefits of these high-energy crops for the dairy cow and the implications of growing the crops in relation to production costs, weed control, effect on the management of the farm and nutrient requirements from the available on-farm manure sources.

Performance of two dairy systems at Ty Gwyn in the 1999-2000 period

Converting to organic farming involves three main stages: pre-conversion planning, physical and financial management of the farm during the conversion period and then achieving full organic status and a premium price for the organic milk. However, even after full organic status is achieved there will be changes to the standards defined for organic production that may require changes in the management of the farm. There is also the potential to improve the physical production, financial income and efficiency of nutrient utilisation within the individual farm system.

Currently IGER is investigating the potential output from two contrasting organic production systems, including identifying management practices that can improve the physical and financial performance of the organic dairy farm. During 1999 the Ty Gwyn dairy farm was divided into two separate systems and the main parameters defined for the two systems are shown below:

System A:
- A total land area of 51.0 ha (including land for grazing, conservation and cereal grain production).
- Moving to self sufficiency with minimal or no purchased feed.
- Maintaining a crop rotation that includes the production of forage from grass/clover swards, cereals for grain and red clover as a protein source.
- Feeding the dairy cows high-forage diets supplemented with a low quantity of cereals.
- A target stocking rate of <1.4 LSU/ha.

System B:
- A total land area of 43.5 ha for grazing and conservation.
- Feeding purchased concentrates to balance home-grown forages.
- Maintaining an all-forage rotation based on grass/clover swards for grazing and conservation and spring barley for conservation as whole-crop cereals.
- Feeding diets to maximise profitability within the standards required for organic production.
- A target stocking rate of 1.7 to 1.8 LSU/ha.

The physical division of Ty Gwyn into two units has included allocating the individual fields to each system based on soil type, P and K status and sward type. The Holstein-Friesian cows in the herd were allocated to each system to achieve a balance between the groups in relation to origin (homebred or purchased), age, milk yield, milk quality, calving date, reproductive status and health. Work was carried out to modify the existing buildings and allow the slurry and parlour washings to be collected separately for the two systems. Both the slurry and solid manure are being utilised for crop production within the systems from which they were produced.

Results from the first year of production

To meet the requirements for cereal grain in System A, both spring barley and triticale have been grown with the aim of producing grain yields of 3 to 3.5 t of grain/ha and providing 0.5 t of grain per cow for feeding. The total milk production of 6709 litres/ha in System A was calculated as the total milk production divided by the total land area (i.e. including both the forage and cereal production areas). In System A the level of purchased concentrate feeding was influenced by the 23.6 t of grain produced from the spring barley and triticale crops. This resulted in a total of 0.4 t/cow of purchased feed being fed, significantly lower than the 1.3 t/cow fed in System B, which included brewers grains fed as a buffer feed during the summer period. During the year home-grown feed contributed 99.2% and 80.3% of the total feed requirements, and forage 94.0% and 81.1% to the total diet of the cows, in Systems A and B, respectively.

The total milk yield of cows in System B was higher compared with the yield of cows in System A (Table 7.6). However, the production of milk from forage was significantly higher from cows in System A. Differences in milk quality between the systems were small, but mathematical modelling of the current production data is showing differences between cows in relation to milk quality and shape of lactation curve. No major health problems were recorded in either system during the first year of the study. The number of cases of clinical mastitis was low in both systems with no cases found during the dry period.

Table 7.6   Performance of the two herds at Ty Gwyn in Year 1

	System A	System B
Average number of cows/herd	58	55
Stocking rate (LSU/ha)	1.44	1.67
Concentrates (t/cow)	0.4	1.3[1]
Total milk production per ha (litres)	6709	9232
Rolling average annual milk yield per cow (litres)	4703	5530
Average 305-day lactation milk yield per cow (litres)	5407	6093
Milk from forage:		
Rolling average annual yield per cow (litres)	3895	2707
Average 305-day yield per cow (litres)	4441	2950
Milk fat (%)	4.12	3.96
Milk protein (%)	3.30	3.33
Margin over purchased feed:		
£/cow	1335	1463
p/litre	28.4	26.5

[1] Includes brewers grains fed as a buffer feed in the summer

Conclusions

The results in Table 7.6 are from the first year of the study and changes in both the physical and financial performance of the two systems may be recorded in the future. The management of System A is both more complicated and the output more influenced by seasonal weather variations than for System B. For System A the challenges include achieving a balance between the areas allocated for grain and forage production and ensuring sufficient forage is available for both grazing and conservation. With a lower stocking rate and minimal purchased feed the nutrient supply within System A is significantly lower compared with the nutrient availability in System B. Meeting the nutritional requirements of the dairy cows from diets based on home-grown feed is also critical in relation to production, health and fertility as the inputs of concentrates will remain low to achieve a higher level of self sufficiency. Management of System B is easier although any major changes in the future price of purchased organic feeds will have a significant effect on the financial performance of the system.

REFERENCES

Hovi, M (1997) Mastitis. *New Farmer and Grower* Summer 1997, pp 18.

Weller, R.F. (1999) Forage for beef and dairy cattle. *Organic Farming*. Summer 1999. Number 62, 12-13.

Weller, R.F. and Cooper, A. (1995) The effect of the grazing management of mixed swards on herbage production, clover composition and animal performance. *Proceedings of the British Grassland Society Occasional Symposium No.29*, Harrogate, UK 1995.

Weller, R.F. and Cooper, A.(1996) The health status of dairy herds converting from conventional to organic dairy farming. The *Veterinary Record*. 139: 141-142.

Weller, R.F. and Davies, D.W.R. (1998) Somatic cell counts and incidence of clinical mastitis in organic milk production. *The Veterinary Record* 143: 365-366.

Weller, R.F. & Bowling, P.J. (2000) Health status of dairy herds in organic farming. *The Veterinary Record* 146: 80-81.

Weller, R.F., Cooper, A. & Padel, S. (1996)Animal production during conversion. In: : R J Haggar & S Padel (eds) *Conversion to organic milk production.* IGER Technical Bulletin No.4, 84-96.

Weller, R.F., Cooper, A., Theobald, V.J. & Miles, S. (1996b) The potential of high forage diets for the organic dairy herd. *Proceedings of the 11th International Silage Conference,* September 8-11th 1996, Aberystwyth, UK.

Further information

Case study 1: Abbey Home Farm - Contact: John Newman
Case study 2: Ty Gwyn Farm. IGER - Contact: Richard
Weller

Chapter 8

Organic Beef Production: Two Case Studies of Rearing/Finishing Enterprises

D. SHELL[1] AND D. YOUNIE[2]

[1] *Godscroft, Abbey St Bathans, Duns, Berwickshire, TD11 3TY*
[2] *SAC, Craibstone Estate, Bucksburn, Aberdeen AB21 9YA*

INTRODUCTION

Beef cattle play a major role on most successful organic farms in the UK. In addition to contributing to economic viability and utilising the main fertility-building crop, grass/clover leys, the animals also contribute through the provision of farm-yard manure. At present, in the early years of the new century, the supply of home-produced organic beef is unable to satisfy demand, and so there is importation of a product which could be produced in the UK efficiently and at competitive prices. There is a major challenge, therefore, for UK organic producers to expand production and to substitute these imports. This paper examines the requirements of the standards and illustrates the practicalities and profitability of organic beef production based on experiences from two Scottish beef enterprises over a period of 10 to 15 years. The case study farms are as follows:

a) **Godscroft**, Duns, Berwickshire, farmed by Duncan Shell, which is a 400 hectare mixed upland farm with spring cereals, temporary and permanent grassland, 1100 breeding ewes and 86 suckler cows taking progeny to finish.

129

b) Scottish Agricultural College farms at **Tulloch**, Aberdeen and **Woodside**, Elgin. Tulloch is a 65 ha mixed upland unit with 45 suckler cows and 200 breeding ewes, with weaned calves being finished at the 57 hectare lowland ley/arable unit at Woodside.

ORGANIC STANDARDS FOR BEEF PRODUCTION

The major elements of the standards for beef production are common to all livestock enterprises and are determined by EU Regulation 1804/1999 (CEC, 1999) at European level and by UKROFS standards (UKROFS, 2000) at UK national level. These are outlined below:

* Where there are both organic and conventional units on the same farm, it is prohibited to have the same livestock species on both units.
* No grazing of non-organic livestock on organic land, except for a limited period only (120 days per annum).
* Land and livestock can be converted simultaneously, allowing calves born during the conversion period to be sold with full organic status as soon as the 24-month conversion period for the land is completed.
* Livestock must have access to pasture during the growing season.
* Housed animals must be provided with bedding - totally slatted systems are prohibited.
* At least 60% of livestock diets, on a dry matter basis, must be home-produced.
* Ruminant livestock must be fed on a diet comprising at least 60% green forage, on a daily dry matter basis (i.e. maximum 40% concentrates).
* Livestock diets must be based principally on organically-produced feedstuffs but a small proportion can be of

130

conventional origin (maximum 10% of annual dry matter intake).

* Feeds derived from genetically modified organisms, fishmeal, urea and solvent-extracted feeds are prohibited.
* Livestock health policy must be based on preventative **management strategies** - aimed at minimising disease challenge and maximising the animal's ability to withstand the challenge; no routine treatment of healthy animals with drugs, **except in the case of a known farm problem**. However, chemotherapy of individual sick animals **is** permitted, although withdrawal periods are extended. A maximum of three courses of treatment is permitted per individual per annum.

CHOICE OF BREED

In 1986 the Godscroft herd contained approximately 70 cows of mixed origin but with a large proportion of Simmental genetics. These were predominantly July-August calvers to Simmental or Charolais bulls. They were wintered on silage, complemented by home grown and processed grain. Calves were subsequently sold as store animals in the following autumn having been wintered indoors.

In 1992 a decision was made to establish a pure-bred self contained herd. The choice of the Aberdeen Angus as a dam breed and the decision to adopt a pure pedigree breeding policy was made for several reasons. A cow of small to medium mature size is better able to maintain itself on grass alone and cope with a relatively short Scottish grazing season. As indicated above, the organic livestock standards emphasise the need to select breeds well-adapted to the environmental conditions of the farm.

131

Ease of calving, satisfactory temperament, proportionate milk production, and the production of a premium beef animal were also significantly attractive traits, as was natural polling, particularly in a low input labour situation. Other breeds may meet many or possibly all of these objectives but the Angus has performed well.

Cross-breeding would give hybrid vigour advantages and allow greater biological efficiency potentially by using a larger crossing sire on to the smaller Angus. However, this would reduce the opportunity to increase herd size and achieve genetic progress, and potentially to sell breeding stock. Once the herd has achieved the target size of 200 cows, a terminal sire of continental breed may be selected for poorer females.

In addition to its genetic suitability to the grass-based organic system, the Aberdeen Angus breed has an additional high-quality image which complements the organic brand image.The suckler cow herd at SAC Tulloch is also based on Aberdeen-Angus, but cross-bred cows are used in order to take advantage of hybrid vigour, in particular to enhance milk production. The smaller farm size at Tulloch restricted opportunities to establish a self-contained herd, but this is undoubtedly a highly desirable objective in terms of minimising health problems. Aberdeen Angus and Simmental bulls are used as terminal sires.

REPRODUCTIVE PATTERN

At Godscroft, March-April calving has been adopted in order to take maximum advantage of the seasonal cycle. Calving in spring has several notable advantages for organic beef production:

- For an outwintered herd, spring calving ensures that all animals carried into winter are approximately six months old at least and better able to stand up to harsh weather.
- Cows approach calving at the point of the calendar year when they are at their leanest, thus reducing dystocia problems.
- Excess milk production incidence is reduced
- Fly problems do not exist, reducing mastitis incidence
- Calving can take place outdoors with reduced risk of severe weather (albeit with a greater risk than summer calving).
- Cows meet spring grass peak growth rates at their lowest body condition and an increasing demand for milk from the calf. This makes them very biologically efficient.
- A peak milk yield on grass alone is achieved at peak grass productivity, thus maximising annual lactation yield.
- Fertility is maximised by a rising plane of nutrition
- Calves begin grazing when grass productivity, quality and palatability is high
- Cows can lay down significant body reserves during the latter part of the grazing season, reducing winter feed requirements by allowing a gradual controlled loss of that stored body condition, which also may assist with body heat insulation.
- Weaning takes place around late December to late January. The date of weaning is related to fine-tuning of dam body condition, thus leaving an independent calf well able to cope with a forage diet.
- Weaned calves approach their second grazing season with good frames and moderate to thin body condition again allowing maximum use to be made of grazed grass. This permits sale of finished animals to take place from grazed grass alone in September, October and November.

At Tulloch, calving is slightly later, from late April to early July, in order to match the cows' nutrient requirements with the late onset of unfertilised spring growth on this north facing farm. Neverthless, many of the advantages of spring calving outlined above also apply to early summer calving. Cows with calves at foot are housed in late October, with weaning taking place in late February. Weaned calves are then transported to Woodside, being turned out to grass in late April, housed again in October for finishing between November and April.

On the other hand, whilst spring/early summer calving may be the ideal option biologically, a degree of autumn calving is likely to be necessary in large herds in order to spread labour requirement and to meet the need for a continuous, year round supply of beef to the butcher, although this latter can also be approached by modifying diet and breed choice.

GRASSLAND MANAGEMENT

As with any extensive ruminant enterprise, and particularly in organic systems, good grassland management is fundamental. The Godscroft herd rotates around the farm following and being followed by sheep on an annual basis. This allows an alternating clean grazing system to be adhered to, which undoubtedly benefits both species but probably more specifically the sheep. At Tulloch a similar alternating sheep/cattle clean grazing is followed, on two blocks of permanent, uncuttable land. All stock are generally removed from areas to be grazed in the following year by late November/December (at Godscroft) or by late January (at Tulloch). This allows an essential recovery period for grassland.

An early spring period without any grazing pressure is of great significance in enhancing April production and indeed seasonal production of grass. Under a traditional low-intensity continuous winter/early spring grazing regime, any growth and particularly growth by vigorous early palatable grasses is promptly removed by hungry mouths (which incidentally also have a high maintenance requirement, having to seek far and wide for small reward). This has the effect of reducing the photosynthetic capacity of the pasture and increasing pressure on early growing and palatable species, thus leading to progressive degeneration of the sward, as well as the more immediate effect of a shortage of spring grazing. Establishing a good grass cover in spring, and maintaining the self-discipline of withholding stock until the sward is ahead of future demand (both as a result of increased growth rate and a buffer or wedge of available grass), pays very large dividends. It also makes turnout date from winter sacrifice areas particularly pleasurable.

After a disciplined start to the grazing season, it is important that the sward is maintained correctly. At Tulloch, with a relatively later calving, stock are turned out directly onto their main summer grazing at a fairly heavy stocking rate of approximately 3.5 cows per hectare in May/June. There is no spring grazing of silage fields and the first cut is taken in late June, followed by a second cut in mid-August.

At Godscroft all inbye grassland fields are available for grazing by cattle or sheep in early spring, to allow acceleration of growth of the main summer grazing fields, even at the cost of later and possibly lower yields of conserved grass from silage fields. Stocking rate of cows during April is approximately 2 to 2.5 cows/ha, increasing to 3 cows/ha in May/June. Lower silage yields deplete soil reserves less and allow faster regeneration of the sward after cutting. Maximising silage yield is less essential on this farm because of the availability of alternative winter feeds such as straw and turnips. Topping of grassland maintains herbage quality by removing seed heads and encouraging development of new tillers. Topping also serves a useful weed control purpose in preventing weeds from seeding. It is worth while spending time to level the soil carefully during grass establishment, in order to facilitate topping in later years with a wide mower at rates of up to 6 hectares per hour.

WINTER FEEDING

As indicated above, one of the main features of the organic standards is a minimum proportion of forage in the diet of ruminant animals, reflecting the physiological adaptation of ruminants to forage consumption and digestion. The 60% minimum of forage essentially rules out barley beef systems, without penalising traditional grass-based livestock systems. Quite apart from any physiological or health reasons for minimising concentrate use, organic cereals and concentrates are very expensive and their use should be minimised for financial reasons also. Concentrate use can be minimised, and reliance on grass and forage maximised, by careful choice of breed and reproductive pattern, as indicated above.

At Tulloch, cows and calves are housed in late October. Cows receive silage and minerals, plus straw. Calves also receive a daily creep feed of 500gm organic cereal, minerals plus seaweed meal. After weaning the feeding rate of cereal is increased to 1kg per head perday. In their second (finishing) winter, cattle are fed silage *ad libitum* plus 2 to 3 kg/day organic cereal plus minerals. For finishing heifers, cereal feeding may be delayed or reduced in order to avoid finishing too early at light carcase

136

weights or at high fat cover. No purchased protein is fed at any time, either to cow, calf or finishing animal. Total cereal consumption per head is 120kg for calves in their first winter and 325kg for finishing animals.

Winter-feeding of cattle at Godscroft usually starts around 1 December although earlier feeding can be precipitated by snowfall or indeed pasture damage in extremely wet conditions. Cows are fed the poorest quality silage or hay until turnout in spring. Weaned calves learn to eat silage alongside their mothers then after weaning receive a diet of best quality silage and in some years, grade-out swedes. Fattening animals are finished exclusively on grazed grass, with an occasional late-finishing animal receiving some silage.

WEANING MANAGEMENT AND LIVESTOCK HANDLING

Under the system at Godscroft, calves remain with their mothers in early winter on a sacrifice area of land to be arable-cropped the following year, while they continue to benefit from milk production and learn to eat silage. They are then separated from their mothers (late December-late January) by well-maintained electric fencing and continue to receive silage while stress levels are minimised by continued nose to nose contact with their mothers. Quiet handling of calves at this behaviourally vulnerable stage is useful (e.g. by walking amongst them with slow deliberate strides and calming voice). In an extensive system such as this, lack of contact with humans can cause behavioural problems in mature animals. Another opportune time for contact presents itself when heifers are with a bull for the first time. The group can also be walked amongst quietly and possibly introduced to a token amount of cereal fed on the ground to create a positive association with humans.

HEALTH STRATEGIES

Few health problems are experienced in the extensive beef systems described here. At Godscroft, cattle are never housed and clinical respiratory problems are exceedingly rare. Pneumonia is experienced occasionally at Tulloch and affected animals are treated with antibiotic.

Historically it has been assumed that young cattle at Godscroft have accumulated a worm burden over the first grazing season. Accordingly, all animals under 12 months old have been routinely wormed once, with a benzimidizole, 24 hours before turnout onto spring grazing. This policy is currently under review following the introduction of new livestock standards after the implementation of EU Regulation 1804/1999 (CEC, 1999).

At Tulloch, cows receive no routine veterinary treatment. Calves have been routinely treated with lungworm vaccine before transfer to Woodside for turnout in their second summer, since this has proved to be a problem on this farm. Alternating clean grazing systems with sheep are in operation at both Tulloch and Woodside and so no routine worming treatment is given, either at housing at the end of their first season or prior to turnout in their second season. Signs of scour are very rare.

However, on both Godscroft and at Tulloch/Woodside, it is routine practice to supplement diets with trace elements. At Tulloch this has been supplied as a specially formulated mineral powder fed to all cattle with silage, whilst at Godscroft it has taken the form of a slow-release trace element bolus for the cows and second season calves, along with free access minerals. This has been justified by chronically low levels of copper, selenium and cobalt in the farm area, and indeed is permitted by the organic standards where deficiencies can be proved by soil, forage, or blood analysis. Livestock diets must not be deficient in essential elements, since this will lead not only to poor thrift but also increased susceptibility to disease. This is particularly important where the farm is self-sufficient and all livestock feed comes from the farm itself, with no imported feed being used.

External parasites have not posed a serious challenge at Godscroft, although lice are a threat when any animals are introduced. Lice are also the only external parasite experienced at Tulloch, in housed animals. Where external parasites such as lice are controlled, it is important to note that cypermethrin ("Spot On") rather than ivermectins should be used. The standards prohibit the use of ivermectins because of concerns that their very persistent and residual nature may be responsible for reducing soil microbial and insect life on which organic farming is so dependent.

LIVESTOCK PERFORMANCE

The organic livestock standards are aimed at achieving good levels of performance but not at pushing animals to the limit of their genetic potential through the use of high nutrient density diets and supported by high inputs of veterinary medicines. The animal performance at Godscroft and Tulloch/Woodside reflects this, comparing satisfactorily with conventional similarly managed units, without being spectacular (Table 8.1).

Table 8.1 Physical performance of cattle at Godscroft (2000)
and Tulloch/Woodside (mean 1995 to 1999)

	Godscroft	Tulloch/Woodside	
	(Steers)	(Steers)	(Heifers)
Age at slaughter (months)	17.4	18 to 22	17 to 21
Average carcase weight (kg)	265	287	248
Average price (£/kg DCW)	2.44	2.37	2.33

DCW = Dead Carcass weight

It should be noted that the price of finished beef animals has risen during 2000, with an R4L carcase attracting a price of £2.70 per kg DCW. At Tulloch/Woodside over the period 1995 to 1999, 71% of all finishing animals achieved a carcase grading of R4L or above.

At present, nearly all heifers at Godscroft are retained for breeding. Eventually, when heifers are not all needed for herd expansion, problems may arise with over-finished/underweight animals. This may require an extended retention and modification to management to increase mature size, as occurs at Woodside.

The profitability of organic beef systems has been shown to equal or better similar conventional systems. Younie and Mackie (1996), reporting a four-year beef systems comparison (1989-93), showed that gross margin per head of an organic 18-month beef system was £49, 30% greater than that of an intensively fertilised (270kgN/ha) conventional 18-month system. Gross margins per hectare from the two systems were virtually identical because of the lower stocking rate on the organic system. Since then, the widening of the organic premium from 14% to nearer 30% and the introduction of the Organic Aid Scheme has swung the advantage to the organic system. Calculation of gross margins for a finished steer enterprise based on physical data from the SAC Tulloch/Woodside organic finishing enterprise, at current (2001) organic (O) and conventional (C) prices, is shown in Table 8.2. This does not include Organic Aid Scheme payments.

Gross margins for beef enterprises at Godscroft are complicated by the retention of most of the heifers for herd expansion purposes. However, the gross margins for the 1999 marketing season were £386/head and £357/head for suckler cow and finishing beef enterprises respectively (excluding forage costs).

Both of the enterprises described here were rearing/finishing units. At present there is a considerable shortage of organic suckled calves for purchase, and this may be one of the major barriers to expansion of organic beef finishing enterprises on low-ground farms.

CONCLUSIONS

The organic standards define the framework within which the beef production system must be designed. These standards encourage a forage-based system, using breeds which are well adapted to the farm situation, and aim to minimise health problems by minimising stress, good diet and restricted stocking rates. In practice, in the two case studies described here, very few health problems existed and animal performance compared well with conventional forage-based beef production systems. Gross margins for organic beef are considerably higher than for

Table 8.2 Gross margin (GM) of organic and conventional finishing steer enterprises, 2001.

		Organic			Conventional	
Output	kg	Price/unit	£/head		Price/unit	£/head
Sale value	287	£2.60/kg DCW	746		£1.90/kg DCW	545
Beef Special Premium			76			76
Extensification prem.			21			21
Slaughter premium			17			17
Less: Purchased calf	280	£1.35/kgLW	378		£1.05/kgLW	294
Total output			482			365
Variable costs						
Feed	400	£170/t	68		£60/t	24
Vet, med			6			8
Bedding			35			25
Haulage			8			8
Commision			11			11
Total variable costs			128			76
GM per head,excluding forage			**354**			**289**
Forage costs		£61	61		£91	91
GM per head, including forage			**293**			**198**
Area used (including silage)		0.35 hectares			0.28 hectares	
GM per hectare (£)			**837**			**707**

DCW = Dead carcass weight, LW = Live weight

conventional beef, on a per head and a per hectare basis, because of good price premiums. Organic beef offers relatively few technical difficulties but major financial opportunities for farmers.

REFERENCES

CEC (1999) *Council Regulation No 1804/1999 supplementing Regulation No 2092/91 on organic production.* Official Journal of the European Communities, 42, L222, 1-28.
UKROFS (2000). *UKROFS Standards for Organic Livestock Production.* United Kingdom Register of Organic Food Standards, London, August 2000.
Younie D. & Mackie C.K. (1996). Factors affecting profitability of organic, low-input and high-input beef systems. In Parente G., Frame J. & Orsi S. (eds) *Grassland and Land Use Systems*, 16th meeting of European Grassland Federation, Grado, Italy, September 1996, 879-882.

Chapter 9

Organic Sheepmeat Production

R. KEATINGE

ADAS Redesdale, Rochester, Otterburn, Newcastle-upon-Tyne, NS19 1SB

INTRODUCTION

Towards the latter end of the 1990s, organic sheep producers began to reap the benefit of the surge in market demand for organic produce. The economic downturn encouraged conventional farmers to look at the organic option, even if only as a short-term measure. Approximately eighty percent of the land area put into conversion under the MAFF Organic Farming Scheme has been extensively managed grassland. However, for the growth in organic lamb production to be sustained, infrastructure needs to be further developed, market share expanded, production systems refined, and specific technical constraints overcome to accommodate the continuing evolution in organic standards.

THE DECISION TO CONVERT

Before deciding to convert, the physical and financial implications should be considered fully. The outcome will depend very much on the individual farm, existing balance of enterprises, stocking densities, market potential, and whether additional agri-environmental or extensification payments can be drawn down to complement livestock sales. Impacts must be realistically assessed on a whole farm basis, taking account of other farm enterprises; for example, an expansion in cattle numbers may be required to improve parasite control. The opportunity cost of conversion for an extensive hill farm could be very low, relative to a lowland farm where grassland output may be 20 to 25% lower following conversion. Establishing a new sheep enterprise where none previously existed incurs significant costs in stock, facilities, labour and expertise. Once the decision is made, the lead-in time provided by the grassland conversion period should be used wisely, to develop marketing strategies, establish links with store lamb finishers, or develop appropriate flock health strategies.

PRODUCTION SYSTEMS

The beneficial effect on soil fertility from the integration of sheep and arable is well recognised (Ryder, 1983). In conventional production, this integration has become less common, as arable farmers specialise in simpler cereal rotations. Sheep production has tended to retract to its traditional strongholds in more marginal areas in the hills and uplands, or grassland farms towards the south and west of the UK, where sheep traditionally form part of a mixed farming system. In theory, the easiest systems to convert will be very extensive hill sheep farms, or mixed farms with a good mix of existing enterprises. Lowland or upland farms, heavily stocked mainly by sheep, are difficult to convert due to the risk of internal parasites. Some change in the balance of enterprises is inevitable as part of the conversion process.

Production will be governed by site-specific factors such as climate, topography, physical resources (cropping, labour, housing etc), as well as external factors such as market outlets, the availability of organically-produced feed, or constraints imposed by the organic standards for disease control or away-wintering. In the UK, sheep production is closely related to the seasonality of grass production - a feature accentuated by organic management (Newton, 1993). Lambing dates are guided by spring growth patterns – generally February/March in the southwest; April/May in the northeast. In extensive hill and upland systems, optimum production is likely to come from traditional lambing dates, and the sale of lambs as stores. May lambing has become more fashionable, even on lowland farms, as a means of reducing overheads, variable costs and diseases of housing. If continuity of supply is the objective, a range of lambing date may be required, provision made for autumn/winter finishing, or links developed with other farms for store lamb finishing.

Successful home-finishing will depend on maintaining good parasite control and providing additional feed resources after weaning e.g. silage aftermath, dairy pasture, or specific forage crops such as stubble turnips, undersown grass/clover, or swedes. Good margins are currently achievable from a store lamb finishing enterprise on dairy pasture or catch crops.

Given the 80 pure breeds and crosses of sheep available in the UK, there is no shortage of genetic diversity or potential adaptability for local conditions. With appropriate management, many of these options can be made to work in an organic system. In hill situations, hardy pure-bred types can be drawn from existing local breeds. More prolific crossbred ewes are suitable for better upland, as well as lowland farms. For January/February lambing, a proportion of Dorset or Suffolk will normally be required. The standards currently permit up to 20% of the flock to be purchased annually from non-organic sources. Whenever possible, a closed flock policy is recommended in order to provide better bio-security and, theoretically, the opportunity for genetic selection according to individual farm circumstances. Using crossbred sheep, a structured self-replacing breeding programme is difficult to follow, unless a nucleus flock of pure bred animals is maintained, or crossbred animals are purchased directly, preferably from another organic farm. On organic farms, dual- purpose breeds such as the Lleyn or Clun can have advantages in providing a balance of prolificacy, meat characteristics, and a simpler replacement policy. Larger flocks may be run in family lines, with home-bred rams rotated across families to avoid inbreeding. The potential to meet carcass weight and conformation specifications is important to the value of finished lambs reflecting, the type and quality of terminal sire used.

NUTRITION

Forage production and utilisation is the key to organic lamb production. High forage intakes (grazed or conserved) make for a simpler feeding system, increasing total energy/protein intake, permitting greater latitude in concentrate feeding (within a 60:40 forage to concentrate ratio) and simplifying protein supplementation. Good quality forage not only contains more energy per unit of feed, but being more digestible than poor quality forage, greater quantities are consumed. High clover swards have been shown to improve the growth rate of conventional lambs by up to 30% after weaning (Davies and Hopkins, 1996). Organic lambs fed on clover silage grew 20% faster than lambs fed conventional silage (Keatinge and Murray, 1994).

Techniques to improve the accuracy of rationing, such as feed analysis, body condition scoring, pregnancy scanning, and the use of sward height guidelines, will find equal application in organic farming. For most of the production cycle, maintaining the minimum forage:concentrate ratio required by the organic standards will not compromise health and welfare. The greatest nutritional challenge will be to twin or triplet bearing ewes, during the last month of pregnancy and the first month of lactation. By matching lambing date to the expected pattern of ⚑ grass growth, the requirement for supplements can be reduced significantly. May lambing requires little or no concentrate input.   how?

For a twin-bearing ewe (75 kg liveweight), lambing in March and fed good quality (67D) silage, approximately 10 to 12 kg of concentrates are required the last three weeks of pregnancy. With poor quality hay (55D), it will not be possible to feed similar animals within a 60:40 forage:concentrate ratio without significant weight loss. In these circumstances, the options are to purchase better quality material for use in late pregnancy, or to adopt a flat rate system of concentrate feeding to reduce the peak of concentrate input, or to feed roots (e.g. potatoes) as an additional energy source (Keatinge, 1994).

Potential sources of protein include full-fat (whole) soyabeans (certified GM free), peas or field beans. Mineralised beans have been used successfully as the sole concentrate supplement for pregnant ewes, and as the supplement for lambs finished on silage (Murray and Keatinge, 1994). A combination of blood, soil and herbage analyses can be used to provide a picture of trace element status. When compared with theoretical requirements for various categories of livestock, a mineral and trace element supplement can be purchased or commissioned, appropriate to specific farm circumstances.

Currently, there is a shortage of organic cereals and 70% of the UK requirement for organic feed cereals is imported. Existing derogations allow for the use of up to 10% of non-organic feedstuffs calculated on an annual basis (a maximum of 25% on a daily basis). Within these limits priority is usually given to protein, minerals and trace element supplements, which may be difficult to obtain organically. There is also a lack of fully organic specialist products e.g. sheep feed blocks. While certified organic feeds remain scarce, economics will make the use of conventionally-produced acceptable feeds attractive. However over time, there will be progressive pressure to feed 100% organically produced feedstuffs.

FLOCK HEALTH

Health is often seen as a significant challenge to the organic sheep farmer (Roderick and Hovi, 1999). With professional veterinary assistance, a structured health plan should be formulated before conversion. This should consider current disease risk, the potential for control through management, current and future veterinary inputs, and the use of alternative treatments. The plan also fulfils a useful function in formalising what will ultimately be acceptable to the certifying body, pre-empting potential problems and agreeing acceptable approaches before an incident actually occurs.

Organic farming poses interesting questions about the development of disease, the host/parasite relationship, and the effect of external and internal factors on the immune system. The standards emphasise prevention through management, nutrition and the reduction of stress. Biosecurity, through physical barriers or the careful introduction of purchased stock, is important in protecting against diseases such as enzootic abortion, orf and sheep scab. Membership of national flock health schemes is another option to formally underline flock health status. In most circumstances, management will need to change progressively - over a period which might extend beyond the period of grassland conversion. A minimum level of veterinary intervention will often be required, depending on farm history and local disease patterns. Measures for ectoparasite control are usually needed on a seasonal basis. Footrot may be a problem, which requires a concerted effort to eradicate. Conditions such as tick-borne disease, fluke and certain trace element deficiencies are locally endemic in more marginal areas. The standards stipulate that where treatment is necessary the most appropriate product (chosen on the basis of efficacy, welfare, persistency and ecotoxicology) may be used with few absolute exceptions, notably organophosphate dips. On veterinary advice, many organic farmers continue to use vaccination against clostridial infection, while others have sought to reduce or remove it from their flocks.

Controlling internal parasites is a particular challenge, even with more moderate stocking rates and often a better balance of enterprises than on conventional farms. Clean grazing systems have been developed to reduce the challenge from roundworms (MAFF, 1983), but due to perceived greater inflexibility have not been taken up by conventional producers (Davies et al, 1996). These systems also rely on the strategic use of anthelmintic, typically before animals were put onto clean pasture. While clean grazing principles should underpin parasite control (Keatinge, 1996), organic producers must make further refinements to minimise or eliminate anthelmintic from the system (Soil Association, 2000). To this end, the most successful producers manage very extensive systems, or mixed systems at moderate stocking rates, where the movement of stock and the crops available between and within seasons are carefully organised to promote good animal nutrition and avoid a rapid rise in parasite burden. With parasites such as roundworms, the objective should not be to eliminate the parasite, but to achieve a level and speed of exposure which encourages the development of immunity.

Recently, a framework has been developed to explain the relationship between protein nutrition and the rise in ewe faecal egg output at lambing (Coop and Kyriazakis, 1999). Organic sheep appear to carry a wider range of roundworm species (Bob Coop – personal communication), some of which are non-pathogenic, and may partly explain an apparent greater tolerance to parasite burdens measured conventionally through faecal egg output. Controlling internal parasites without anthelmintics is currently the focus of MAFF-funded research (MAFF Project OFO185). Furthermore, there is now considerable interest amongst farmers in using repeated faecal egg counts as a more accurate genetic selection for worm resistance (Stear *et al.*, 1995). Ultimately, it may be possible to use genetic marking to identify resistant stock.

Homeopathy can have a place in sheep health, on a flock or individual basis (Elliott and Pinkus, 1993). However, little formal research has been conducted. Group application is a practical constraint, particularly in the grazing situation, while relatively low stock values tend to mitigate against individual treatment.

Some promising results have been found in observation studies at ADAS Redesdale (Keatinge, 1996) for orf, ringworm and pasteurella pneumonia. Before using homeopathy, professional advice should be sought to determine the most appropriate products and conditions likely to respond to a homeopathic approach.

INFRASTRUCTURE AND MARKETING

Organic lamb production in 1999 was estimated to be 26,000 lambs (Soil Association, 1999) - a fraction of the seventeen million head slaughtered annually in the UK. At the moment there is little, if any, imported product, but countries as far flung as New Zealand and the Falkland Islands could theoretically enter the marketplace, to take up the seasonal short-fall in supply during February and March.

Historically, the premia achieved for organic lambs were low, ranging from 5 to15% (Elliott *et al.,* 1995). In recent years, price differentials of 30% or more have been achieved, due to the imbalance in supply and demand, and the collapse in conventional prices. Most predictions agree that long-term price differences are likely to narrow to 10 to 20%. While the prospect of a 'butcher's margin' may be attractive, the additional investment, skills and marketing flair required for direct marketing should not be underestimated. Marketing groups have been set up, such as the Organic Livestock Marketing Co-operative and Organic Farmers Scotland Ltd, to provide co-ordination in the market place. A high degree of collective organisation is required to manage the supply chain, agree guide prices, and successfully link store lamb producers, finishers and retailers.

With current supply and demand, organic producers are in a position of relative strength compared with their conventional counterparts. However, there are already some signs of fragmentation in the market, which may still be vulnerable to short-term over-supply against a background of long-term scarcity. The greater rate of conversion amongst hill flocks is soon likely to result in large numbers of store lambs seeking markets on lowland farms during September and October.

Low volume means that the infrastructural difficulties generally associated with the UK sheep industry - seasonality of supply, declining abattoir capacity, distance from markets, are magnified for organic producers, reducing the pace of development, lowering efficiency, increasing handling and distribution costs. With increasing volumes, there is a greater possibility for vertical integration to replicate the traditional stratified structure of the conventional sheep industry. Opportunities are already being taken up for the better linkage of organic farms, either for away-wintering of hoggs or for sourcing of organic breeding stock. In order to improve the supply chain, two pilot organic store lamb sales have been run in 2000, in a further attempt to link formally hill and lowland organic producers.

PHYSICAL AND FINANCIAL PERFORMANCE

Good performance can be obtained from organically managed sheep provided:
- Stocking rates are matched to the potential of the farm.
- Diseases, particularly internal parasites, are controlled.
- A high level of management and livestock husbandry is applied.

Well-managed clover pasture will support a stocking rate of at least 80% of a system receiving 200 kg artificial fertiliser N/hectare (Davies and Hopkins, 1996). Furthermore, most conventional sheep farmers use less than 150 kg N/ha on average, and many could considerably improve the efficiency of grassland utilisation (Davies *et al.*, 1996). Lowland organic beef and sheep systems will carry typical stocking rates of 1.2 to 1.7 Livestock Units (LU)/ha. TEAGASC (1997) reported a stocking rate of 1.4 LU per hectare on an organic lowland beef/sheep research unit. Lamb rearing percentage ranged from 150% to 170%, with mean lamb growth rates to slaughter of up to 224 g/day. Survey data from organic hill and upland farms in the UK (Elliott and Keatinge, 2000) indicate lambing rates of 90 to 135%, and a mean stocking rate of 0.9 Grazing Livestock Units (GLU) per adjusted hectare. This stocking rate may be compared to Farm Business Survey data for conventional farms by the University College of Wales (1.3 GLU) and Newcastle University (0.7 GLU).

Lower weight of lamb produced per hectare is expected to be offset by an improvement in finished prices, and a reduction in variable costs, particularly fertiliser. Other input prices may be more expensive per unit for feed (£180-£200/t currently for cereal) or permitted veterinary products, but overall usage is expected to be lower than on conventional farms. Over three years (1993-1995), TEAGASC (1999), reported mean gross margins per ewe of 41£IR and 42£IR for conventional and organic systems. Gross margin per ewe (before forage costs) of £57 and £37 were reported from the survey of organic farms and University College Wales conventional farms respectively (Elliott and Keatinge, 2000). Most organic farmers participated in some form of agri-environmental scheme, which helped offset the penalties of reduced stocking rate. However, Net Farm Income was higher on the conventional units due to higher fixed costs on the relatively small sample of organic farms. A long-term comparison of organic and conventional systems at ADAS Redesdale has shown good economic performance where similar stocking rates were maintained (£31 vs £34 respectively in 1999), but a significant and ultimately unsustainable fall in individual animal performance. Where stocking rates were reduced in two other organically managed flocks by 15% and 25% respectively, comparable ewe gross margins were £36 and £42. In the latter flock, using additional agri-environmental payments (The Moorland Scheme) a more balanced, yet financially viable, organic system was achieved.

FUTURE PROSPECTS

As a further source of much-needed differentiation in the red meat market, organic production could deliver a combination of local or regional brand identity, added value and agri-environmental objectives. The current production base is small, but capable of growing significantly in response to changes in market conditions and agricultural policy. Many fear that the bubble will burst, the market will saturate and price differentials disappear.

There is no doubt that the greatest challenges faced by the organic sheep industry are not technical, but are found in marketing and infrastructure. The hills and uplands have primed the pump. Whether organic lamb production consolidates, or expands, will depend on organic systems establishing more widely on lowland farms. While stocking rate is still a major determinant of profitability, the increasing weighting towards land rather than livestock based statutory support (through HFA and extensification payments) indicates a further shift towards system- rather than enterprise-based support. Economic viability cannot rely on a high level of price premium. Instead it should be derived from balanced production, combining lower input costs with a modest price differential, and agri-environmental support. Crucially, organic systems must deliver long-term on price, quality, availability, environmental and welfare aspirations of the paying (and voting) public.

REFERENCES

Coop, R.L. & Kyriazakis, I (1999). Nutrition-parasite interaction. *Veterinary Parasitology,* **84** (1999) 187 - 204.

Davies, D.A. & Hopkins, A. (1996) Production benefits of legumes in grassland. In: D Younie (ed.) *Legumes in Sustainable Farming Systems*, Occasional Symposium No 30, British Grassland Society, 1996, p234.

Davies, M., Peel, S., Harley, R., Ellis, S., Merrell, B. & Powell, L.N. (1996). Study to assess the uptake of results generated from grassland *R and D. Project MS1413 - A Review for MAFF Livestock Group,* June, 1996.

Elliott, M & Pinkus, T, (1993) *Homeopathy, The Shepherds Guide.* Published by Ainsworths Homeopathic Pharmacy, 38 New Cavendish Street, London. 1993.

Elliott, J., & Keatinge, R. (2000*) Organic Sheep and Beef Production in the Hills and Uplands* (MAFF Project OFO147) Report of Linked Farms, February 2000.

Elliott, J., Keatinge, R., Powell, L. & Unwin, R. J. (1995) *Finishing store lambs from organic hill and upland farms .* A review prepared for MAFF Agricultural Resources Policy Division, March 1995, 68 pp.

Keatinge, R. (1994) Feeding prolific ewes to UKROFS standards. *New Farmer and Grower,* **41**, Winter 1994, 26-27.

Keatinge, R. (1996) Case studies in homeopathy. *New Farmer and Grower,* November 1996, **52**, p12-13.

Keatinge, R. (1996) *Controlling internal parasites without anthelmintics*. A review prepared or MAFF Conservation and Woodland Policy Division, December 1996, 63pp.

Keatinge, R.. & Murray, W. A. (1994) Finishing performance of hill lambs fed clover rich baled silage to UKROFS standards. *Animal Production*, **58**, 460.

MAFF (1982). Grazing plans for the control of stomach and intestinal worms in sheep and cattle. *Booklet 2154, 1982.*

Murray, W. A. & Keatinge, R. (1994) Beans (Vicia faba) as a finishing supplement for hill lambs under organic management. *Animal Production*, **58**, 480.

Newton, J. (1993) *Organic Grassland.* Chalcombe Publications, Canterbury, 1993.

Roderick, S. & Hovi, M. (1999) *Animal health and welfare in organic livestock systems: identification of constraints and priorities*. Report to MAFF, VEERU Reading, April 1999.

Ryder, M.L. (1983) *Sheep and Man.* Duckworths, London ISBN 0715616552

Soil Association (1999) *The Organic Food and Farming Report 1999*. The Soil Association, Bristol.

Soil Association (2000) *Roundworm control in organic sheep systems*. Technical Guide, The Soil Association, Bristol, 2000.

Stear, M.J., Bairden, K., Duncan, J. L., Gittinby, G., McKellar, Q.A. & Murray, M. & Wallace, D.S. (1995). The distribution of faecal egg counts in Scottish Blackface lambs following natural, predominantly *Ostertagia circumcinta* infection. *Parasitology* **110:** 573-581

TEAGASC (1997) *Organic Calf to Beef/Sheep Production.* Research Investigation. TEAGASC, Johnstown Castle, October 1997.

Chapter 10

Organic Pig Production

A. MARTINS

ADAS Consulting Ltd., ADAS Woodthorne, Wergs Road, Wolverhampton, WV6 8TQ

INTRODUCTION

Organic pig production can be defined as the rearing of pigs on organic land in accordance with the standards laid down by the UK organic Sector Bodies. Although a limited number of non-organic livestock may be brought onto an organic farm, any pigmeat sold as organic must come from pigs which were conceived on organic land and raised in accordance with the standards from conception through to slaughter. Within this paper the requirements of UKROFS and the Soil Association are mentioned. However, the Sector Bodies, which also include the Bio-Dynamic Agricultural Association, Organic Farmers and Growers, the Organic Food Federation and the Scottish Organic Producers Association, should always be consulted as standards are amended over time and consideration needs to be given to possible derogations.

Organic pig production has been developing on commercial farms since the mid 1980s. Formal research in the UK began in 1999 through a three-year project, Optimising Production Systems for Organic Pig Production (OF0169), funded by MAFF with contributions from PIC and Tesco. The research team consists of ADAS Consulting Ltd, Newcastle University, Eastbrook Farm and Eco-Stopes Consultancy. The majority of the research work is being carried out at Eastbrook Farm, with a number of other commercial organic farms providing research facilities, production information and data.

The project, which will be completed by March 2002, is investigating the effect of conventional and traditional breed types, reared under different organic production systems including feed type and housing, on:

- Prolificacy, rearing ability and longevity of sows.
- Growth rate and carcase characteristics of growing pigs.
- Organoleptic qualities of fresh pigmeat and processed product.
- Sward utilisation, animal welfare, manure deposition and parasite levels under alternative paddock systems.
- Welfare of the organic stock.

The project will also appraise the range and nutritional value of feeds available to organic producers, assess the economic implications of organic pig production and establish a Guide to Best Practice for the management of organic pigs.

Currently organic pig production represents less that 1% of total pig production within the UK (Johnson, 2000). However, the market for organically produced pigmeat is growing and a significant proportion of this expanding market is being met by imported product. The substitution of imported product with home-produced organic pigmeat, and satisfying further increases in demand, offer valuable opportunities for UK farmers.

One of the key general principles of organic livestock farming is that it is a land-related activity. Livestock have access to free range areas and stocking levels are limited to ensure the integration of livestock production into the farm and to minimise any form of pollution, soil erosion or other adverse effects on the environment (Soil Association, 2000). These aspects, the market and integration with the land, represent the factors which farmers should consider first when reviewing the opportunities and feasibility of organic pig production for their business.

MARKET OPPORTUNITY

Conventional pigs have typically been marketed as a commodity product with producers being exposed to price variation brought about by imbalances in supply and demand. Organic production represents an opportunity for a more market-facing approach, where expansion in production occurs in order to meet an established market demand. It also provides the opportunity to move away from commodity-based products to branded production. For this to be achieved it is crucial that those proposing to establish an organic herd ensure they have identified their market outlet and established a demand for their product before any capital investment takes place. The outlet could be a farm shop, farmers market, specialist butcher or through an established brand such as Eastbrook Farm Organic Pigs.

AVAILABILITY AND USE OF SUITABLE LAND

Organic pig production is essentially an outdoor activity with both sows and their progeny being integrated into the arable rotation. The ideal land type is flat or gently sloping with light, free draining soils in areas of low to medium rainfall. Where land is less than ideal, modifications to stocking policy can alleviate potential problems. Some land types however, for example steep sloping fields and heavy clays in areas of high rainfall, are unsuitable and should be avoided.

When assessing land requirement, two aspects need to be considered:

◊   ***Rotational land area*** - the total land area which is suitable and available for pigs and across which the pigs will be rotated over a number of years.
◊   ***Stocked land area*** - the land area stocked by pigs at a given point in time.

In determining these two distinct requirements a number of factors need to be considered including the need to ensure that:

◊   Stocking densities do not exceed the limit of 170 kg N/ha/year over the total land area suitable for pigs.
◊   Build-up of parasites is avoided.
◊   Ground cover is maintained to assist in the protection of soil structure and the prevention of soil erosion and nitrate leaching.
◊   Excessive poaching of land and damage to soil structure is avoided.
◊   Effective provision of nutrients to the following crops.

Based on current knowledge the following should be considered:

Rotational land area. The limit to the total amount of manure application over the entire land area available for pigs is 170 kg N/ha/year (UKROFS, 2000). The Soil Association draft revised pig standards (Soil Association, 2000) indicate that one sow and her progeny (18 pigs/annum) to bacon weight (26 weeks) produces 71 kg N per year. This requires a pig to land area ratio of 2.4 sows plus progeny to 1 ha. Actual N production varys between farms, depending on factors such as performance. Allowing for variation in performance a working rule of thumb is a ratio of 2 sows plus progeny to 1 ha.

More generous allowances for total area may be required to meet annual rotation requirements and to ensure ground cover survival. Eastbrook Farm Organic Pigs recommend a total land area of approximately 1 sow plus weaners to 1 acre (0.4 ha) and 1 sow plus weaners/finishers to 2 acres (0.8 ha).

Stocked land area. Stocking policies vary between farms. Some farmers allocate an area of land for a 12 month period (*'set stocked'*) and stock pigs within this area. Typically the total area allocated is 0.125 ha/sow plus progeny. Within this system fresh pasture may be used for some of the paddocks (for example farrowing paddocks). On other organic units a *'wave motion'* is used with the herd moving to fresh pasture every 3 to 4 months. In this system the pigs may move across 0.25 ha or more per sow and progeny during the year (Helen Browning, personal communication). Land ahead of the pigs is typically used for other enterprises in the rotation (for example grazed by sheep) and crops are sown once the pigs have been moved off. Hence the land may have up to 3 farming activities in a year.

Minimum stocking requirements are laid down by the organic standards. The Soil Association September 2000 draft revised pig standards recommends stocking pigs for a maximum of 6 months, with pigs not returning to the same land more than once in four years. For a 200-sow herd utilising a total land area of 100 ha, this would equate to a stocked area, at any point time, of 12.5 ha (0.063 ha/sow plus progeny) with pigs moving across 25 ha (0.125 ha/sow plus progeny) in the year. If an area is allocated to pigs for the entire year then this would equate to

25 ha (0.125 ha/sow). Covering both the *'set stocked'* and the *'wave motion'* systems, Eastbrook Farm recommends an area of 0.16 to 0.2 ha/sow plus progeny per year, finding that this assists in the maintenance of ground cover (Eastbrook Farm, 2000).

BUSINESS OPPORTUNITIES

An organic herd may be established by the land owner or tenant farmer. However in certain circumstances the farmer may wish to take advantage of the benefits organic pigs offer, including nutrient provision and weed control, without having to incur the capital costs associated with the enterprise, the increased management demands and the development of the specialist expertise required. In this situation organic production offers the specialist organic pig producer the opportunity to work in partnership with the farmer.

TECHNICAL ASPECTS OF ORGANIC PIG PRODUCTION

Having established a market and the availability of sufficient organic land consideration is needed of the technical aspects of production. These are, in part, set by the requirements of the sector bodies and, in certain circumstances the specific requirements of the chosen market outlet.

Organic pigs within the rotation

Organic pigs should be effectively integrated into the rotation. Rotations will vary between farms depending on soil conditions, climate etc. Examples of rotations used are detailed below (from Eastbrook Farm (2000):

Year	Rotation 1	Rotation 2
1	Set aside (grass/clover)	Set aside (grass/clover)
2	Pigs/potatoes	Pigs
3	Winter wheat	Potatoes/vegetables
4	Carrots	Spring wheat
5	Spring beans	Spring beans
6	Spring barley undersown	Spring wheat undersown

Where pigs are moved in a *'wave motion'*, crops such as mustard may be grown to maintain green cover, hence reducing nitrate leaching, until the point where a cash crop such as a cereal can be sown. Before deciding on a suitable rotation a nutrient budget, which provides a crude, quantitative assessment of the nutrient gains and losses through a rotation, should be produced. The budget will show the significant contribution made by the pig enterprise to NPK gains.

Breed type

Breed type used will depend upon a number of factors including requirements of the market outlet and the choice of replacement system. Alternative breed types include:

◊ **Pure Bred Stock** Pure bred traditional (e.g. Saddleback, Berkshire and Tamworth) or conventional (Large White, Landrace, Duroc) breeds.

◊ **Crosses** Crosses of traditional and conventional breeds (e.g. Saddleback/Duroc).

◊ **Artificial Lines** Produced by breeding companies (e.g. Camborough 12), offering improved maternal characteristics on the female line and meat characteristic on the male line.

Traditional breeds offer a number of benefits including potential marketing advantages through enhanced public perception and the maintenance of rare breed populations (Johnson, 2000). In terms of performance the maternal productivity of the crossbred stock should exceed those of the pure breeds due to hybrid vigour. In addition, under conventional management practices, the artificial lines would be expected to outperform the traditional and unimproved breeds in terms of sow productivity, growth rate, feed efficiency and reduction in backfat levels.

Research, currently underway to compare performance, carcase characteristics and eating quality of different breed types, aims to differentiate performance under organic conditions. One of the factors which may reduce the performance advantage of the improved breed types is the challenge of achieving the high specification rations required to meet the genetic potential of these stock. These challenges may become more significant as the organic proportion of the feed increases to 100% (Johnson, 2000).

Replacement system

The aim of the organic system is for all breeding animals to be bred and reared organically. However, at present there are derogations to cover situations where sufficient numbers of organically-reared animals are not available. Choice of replacement system is influenced by herd size, breed type, opportunities for buying in organic stock, labour availability and aptitude. Maintenance of herd health also impacts on the decision. As general rule, the less frequently stock are brought in and the lower the number of sources, the less the risk of bringing in disease.

With pure-bred herds the production of on-farm replacements is straight forward, easily integrated into the operation of the unit as a whole and is likely to be the preferred system. Where crosses/lines are used the options include:

◊ Buying-in replacement organic gilts - there is currently limited availability of such stock.

◊ Breeding replacements on-farm from brought-in grand parent or farm bred grandparent stock - both are most suited to herds of 200 sows plus.

◊ A criss-cross system, where subsequent generations are mated to alternative boar breeds - this would not be appropriate for artificial lines as the maternal and sire characteristics would be diluted.

Feed

UKROFS standards state that feed is intended to ensure quality rather than maximising production and require that livestock are fed on organically-produced feedstuffs which have been produced without the use of genetically modified organisms (UKROFS, 2000). A derogation, expiring August 2005, allows up to 20% (as a percentage of annual dry matter) of feed for pigs to come from approved conventional sources. Roughage, fresh or dried fodder or silage must be added to the daily ration.

The production of rations using organically-approved ingredients represents a challenge to the sector. Issues highlighted by Johnson (2000) include the production of diets with sufficiently high specifications (energy and amino acids) to meet the genetic potential of improved stock; the achievement of the required balance of amino acids in the absence of artificial lysine without incorporating excessive protein and accessing sufficient organic protein sources when the derogation on the use of conventional feed expires. Edwards (2001) noted that whilst nutritional information is available for the commonly used conventional feedstuffs, it is still greatly lacking for the wider range of raw materials likely to be used in organic diets with higher forage incorporation.

Edwards (2001) describes factors which need to be considered when formulating diets and provides some example specifications and ingredients for on-farm produced organic rations:

Forage. Organic standards require that pigs receive forage in their diet. This can be achieved by allowing animals to graze at pasture, incorporating dried forage in their compound diet, allowing them *ad libitum* or restricted daily access to products such as silage or root crops with supplementary concentrate, or feeding a complete mixed diet of forage and concentrate in long troughs.

Lactating sows and younger piglets cannot be expected to obtain sufficient nutrients from a forage-based diet and for these stock forage should be viewed as a supplement. Other stock can be fed on higher levels of forage. For growing pigs this will lead to a decrease in daily nutrient intake and reduced growth. Whilst this may be disadvantageous in the early stages of rearing, in the later stages it can help to improve carcass quality by preventing over-fatness.

Feed Manufacture. Feed can be mixed on farm with those ingredients not produced on farm (e.g. minerals and vitamins) being purchased from a specialist supplier of organic feedstuffs. Alternatively compound diets can be purchased from specialist feed compounders.

Diet Specification. The number of diets varies between farms. Some farms use only 2 diets - a lower specification ration fed to dry sows and finishing pigs and a higher specification ration for lactating sows and growers. Others use up to 5 to 6 diets, differentiated into the following stages:

◊ Dry sow & boar ration, also fed to replacement breeding stock from 60 to 70 kg.
◊ Lactating sow ration.
◊ Suckling and newly weaned piglet ration.
◊ Growing pig ration, also fed to replacement breeding stock to 60 to 70 kg.
◊ Finishing pig ration.

Example nutrient specifications are detailed in Tables 10.1 and 10.2. These compound diets are designed to supply the complete daily needs of the animals. Where large amounts of separate forages are fed, the compound diets will need to be modified to complement the composition of the forages.

Diet Formulation. Example diets, suitable for home mixing, are detailed in Table 10.2. Reflecting current organic practice the main protein source in the diets is non GMO soya bean. Home grown protein sources (e.g. peas, beans, rapeseed and lupins) contain anti-nutritive factors which limit their inclusion rate and make the formulation of diets from 100% UK-produced protein crops difficult to achieve. Specialist feed compounders use sophisticated least cost formulation computer programmes to determine the most cost-effective combination of available raw materials to provide the desired diet specification. A handbook on feeding organic pigs is to be produced in 2001 as part of the MAFF project Optimising Production Systems for Organic Pig Production (OF0169, Edwards, 2001).

Table 10.1   Recommended minimum nutrient levels in compound diets.
(Expressed on a meal equivalent basis of 86% dry matter)

	Dry sows and boars	Lactating sows	Suckling & newly weaned piglets	Growing pigs	Finishing pigs
Digestible energy (MJ/kg)	12.5-13.0	13.5-14.0	14.0	13.5	12.5-13.0
Crude protein (%)	13-14	18	20	18	16-17
Lysine (%)	0.5-0.6	0.9	1.3	1.2	0.8-1.0
Methionine +Cysteine (%)	0.3	0.5	0.7	0.7	0.4-0.6
Threonine (%)	0.4	0.6	0.8	0.8	0.5-0.7
Calcium (%)	0.8	0.9	0.8	0.8	0.7
Phosphorus (%)	0.6	0.7	0.6	0.6	0.5
Sodium (%)	0.15	0.15	0.15	0.15	0.15

Organic Pig Production

Table 2. Examples of simple home mixed-diets for different stages of pig production

	Dry sows and boars	Lactating sows	Suckling & newly weaned piglets	Growing pigs	Finishing pigs
Components of diets (% as fed)					
Wheat	-	47.2	55.4	47.5	-
Barley	60.1	-	-	-	45.4
Wheatfeed	25.0	20.0	10.0	10.0	25.0
Peas	10.0	15.0	10.0	15.0	15.0
Soya bean meal (non organic allowance, non GMO)	-	-	-	25.0	12.5
Full fat soya (non organic allowance, non GMO)	2.0	15.0	15.0	-	-
Fishmeal	-	-	8.5	-	-
Calcium carbonate	1.5	1.1	0.8	1.1	1.5
Dicalcium phosphate	0.8	1.2	-	0.9	-
Salt	0.4	0.3	0.1	0.3	0.4
Vitamin & trace element supplement (according to manufacturers recommendation)	0.2	0.2	0.2	0.2	0.2
Nutritional value of diets (as fed)					
Digestible energy (MJ/kg)	12.6	13.9	14.5	13.7	12.9
Crude protein (%)	13	18	21	20	17
Lysine (%)	0.6	0.9	1.3	1.2	0.9
Methionine +Cysteine (%)	0.4	0.5	0.7	0.6	0.5
Threonine (%)	0.4	0.6	0.8	0.8	0.6
Calcium (%)	0.9	0.9	0.8	0.8	0.7
Phosphorus (%)	0.6	0.7	0.6	0.6	0.5
Sodium (%)	0.19	0.15	0.15	0.15	0.19

Management

As with all livestock, the skills and motivation of the staff, attention to detail, good pig observation and prompt action are all key factors in achieving a high standard of animal welfare and productivity. Details regarding feeding policy (Edwards, 2001) and stock management at the different production stages are detailed below. The information on feed policy is based on the use of compound diets with supplementary forage provided.

Service. To achieve consistent levels of productivity all services should be supervised, with boars being removed after service to prevent them from overworking. Preferably each sow should be served with two different boars to cover for any boars with lower levels of fertility. Where labour availability is restricted boars can be paddocked with the sows. In this situation boars can be kept individually with a single sow or a dynamic group of sows where only one of the sows would be expected to be on heat at any time. Alternatively teams of boars (usually 3) can be paddocked with a group of sows (such as a weekly service group) where a number of the sows will be on heat together.

Dry Sows. The appetite of dry sows is generally in excess of their nutrient requirements and as a result stock need to be rationed at this stage to avoid obesity. For typical diets this will require an allowance of 2 to 2½ kg of feed per day in summer and 3 to 3½ kg per day in winter. Good feed distribution is required in order to minimise bullying and achieve equal intake of food within the group.

Farrowing Sows. Ensuring adequate feed intake over the 6 to 8 week lactation period is important. Excessive weight loss will have an adverse effect on piglet and sow performance and welfare. Ad-lib feeders are advised with sows initially being fed to appetite to ensure a healthy appetite is maintained. In the absence of ad-lib feeders sows should be fed twice a day. A typical feeding regime might be to feed 2 to 3 kg feed on the day of farrowing, increasing the allowance by ½ kg each day until appetite level is reached. To promote a good feed intake, it is essential that a plentiful supply of clean water is available close to the farrowing hut. In summer, lactating sows can drink as much as 50 litres of water each day.

Suckling Piglets. Suckling piglets should have access to creep feed from about 3 weeks onwards at which point the sow's milk yield begins to decline. On some farms the piglets are given access to the sow's feed, but piglets will benefit from higher specification diets.

Weaned Sows. The minimum weaning age is 6 weeks, with 8 weeks being recommended (Soil Association, 2000). After weaning, neither food nor water should be withheld from the sows – contrary to traditional opinion, this does not help in 'drying off'. A high quality diet should be fed generously (not less than 3 kg/day) until the sow has been re-bred, as this can help increase the size of the next litter. After mating, the food should be reduced to the typical pregnancy level, but not more than 3 kg/day for the first three weeks of pregnancy unless the sow is in very poor condition. Too much food in the period immediately after mating can reduce the size of the next litter.

Weaned Pigs. If pigs are to be raised in single sex groups, which is advisable, they should preferably be split into males and females at weaning. In addition the size of the group should allow the group to be split down rather then built up at later stages. Although weaners will have been eating solid food for a number of weeks they will still have a bond with the sow. To prevent piglets escaping from their paddocks and returning to the sow it is advisable to keep them in an enclosed area (for example a kennel) for the first two weeks following weaning.

Growers/Finishers. Young growers normally feed *ad libitum* from a specially designed feed hopper. This allows each pig to eat according to its own requirements, and minimises aggression arising from competition for food. With *ad libitum* feeding, enough trough space for 25% of the pigs to eat at the same time is recommended. Pigs can be fed once or twice daily to appetite, but in this case the trough must be long enough for all pigs, including timid ones, to eat happily at the same time.

Finishing pigs can be brought indoors for a maximum of one fifth of their lifetime (UKROFS, 2000). The standards lay down minimum areas for indoor and exercise areas and recommend the use of straw and plentiful natural ventilation (Soil Association, 2000). Housing the finished pig prior to sale offers a number of advantages including better control of feeding and therefore carcase quality, and improved weighing and loading facilities away from the main herd and can be readily disinfected. At this stage it may be necessary to restrict-feed the pigs to control backfat levels. This is more likely to be the case for traditional breeds where feed may need to be restricted from as early as 50 kg. Restriction of feed of typical energy and protein content by about 0.3 kg/day (10 to 12% of *ad libitum* intake) is usually required to reduce backfat thickness at slaughter by 1 mm, and will be associated with a reduction in growth rate of about 100 g/day. If restrict-fed, the trough should allow all pigs to feed at once, and bulky feeds should be provided.

Health

Under organic production the aim is to achieve disease prevention through:

174

◊ Selection of appropriate breeds and strains of animals.
◊ Appropriate husbandry practices.
◊ Use of high quality feed, regular exercise and access to pasture.
◊ Ensuring appropriate stocking densities.

Where disease occurs antibiotic treatment can be given as the welfare of the stock is paramount. However, alternative therapies such as herbal treatments or homeopathy, which is encouraged in organic farming (Aukland, 1997), are preferred if these are effective against the condition. Where antibiotics are used, farmers should take note of the extended withdrawal period and, for repeated treatments, the impact on the organic status of the animal. Treatment must not be withheld, even if that particular animal looses its organic status. Along side any treatment the aim should be to identify factors, within the production system, which might have predisposed the animal to the disease and assess how these factors can be improved.

LABOUR

Labour requirement will depend on herd size, level of mechanisation and management practices. Larger herds are more labour-efficient and for herds of over 200 sows a ratio of 100 sows and progeny to one person is achievable. Smaller herds will require relatively higher levels of labour with a 50 to 70-sow unit requiring one full time person plus relief.

FINANCIAL ASPECTS OF ORGANIC PIG PRODUCTION

Under the Eastbrook Farm Organic Pigs production system a 100-sow herd selling 18 bacon pigs/sow /year could achieve a margin of £220 per sow. The margin is after labour costs, rent and depreciation but before interest charges. The capital investment required is substantial - the initial cost of machinery, equipment and buildings is estimated to be £100,000 and the total value of stock at £80,000. Profitability is extremely sensitive to performance and improvements in numbers sold from 18 to 19.5 pigs per year can increase the margin achieved by £120 per sow/annum. This sensitivity to performance highlights the importance of skilled and effective management as a fall in production to 16.5 pigs would reduce the margin to £100 per sow. Larger herds can benefit from economies of scale leading to potentially greater levels of profitability.

REFERENCES

Aukland, C (1997) *Homeopathy and Organic Farming*, British Organic Farmers, Producer Division of the Soil Association, Bristol.

Eastbrook Farm (2000) *Eastbrook Farm Organic Pig Manual*, 36 Station Road, Framlingham, Suffolk, IP13 9EE

Edwards, S.A. (2001), *Feeding Organic Pigs*: A handbook produced as part of the MAFF project OF0169. University of Newcastle Upon Tyne. (In preparation)

Johnson, A. (2000) *Quality Organic Pork Production*, Society of Feed Technologists, Proceedings 2000 (In press).

Soil Association, (2000) *Organic Pig Production Standards*, Open Draft, September 2000

UKROFS (2000). *UKROFS Standards for Organic Livestock Production*. United Kingdom Register of Organic Food Standards, London, August 2000.

Chapter 11

Organic Egg Production: Consumer Perceptions[1]

C. STOPES[2], R. DUXBURY[3] and R.GRAHAM[4]

[2] Eco-Stopes Consulting, Newbury, RG14 6PP UK
[3] Sainsbury's Supermarkets Ltd., Stamford House, London, SE1 9LL UK
[4] Roy Graham Marketing Research, Bradford on Avon, BA15 1DU UK

INTRODUCTION

Organic poultry production standards in EU member states vary. Specific production parameters are laid out in the EU Livestock Regulation (EU, 1999), which also includes a maximum derogation period of 10 years for systems to meet the new standards. In the UK, some organic sector bodies and UKROFS (the UK control authority) may introduce a higher standard than the EU Regulation, and/or a shorter derogation period.

The EU regulation presumes that livestock production is integrated into the whole organic farming system and is land-based. In the case of poultry, requirements to encourage integration include the rotation and resting of pasture, maximum flock size, manure disposal on the farm or on a

---

[1] An earlier version of this paper was presented at the 13th International Scientific Conference of the International Federation of Organic Agriculture Movements, Basel, Switzerland in August 2000.

linked unit, and a maximum manure application rate equivalent to 170 kg N/ha per annum. Together these requirements militate against the larger fixed house organic poultry systems, which have converted from conventional free-range units.

Approximately one million laying hens produce organic eggs in the UK. Prior to the introduction of the EU Livestock Regulation (EU, 1999) the majority were in fixed houses, including flock sizes of 8,000 to 10,000 in production units which are not 'land based' and are not integrated into the organic farming system. Feed consumption for this level of egg production amounts to 40,000 tonnes per annum approximately three-quarters being imported.

CUSTOMER PERCEPTIONS OF ORGANIC EGG PRODUCTION

Six discussion groups with 7 to 8 members (focus groups), and interviews with free-range (160) and organic (210) egg consumers were completed to assess customers' perceptions about organic egg production. The study was designed to establish the reasons for organic and free-range egg purchases and the importance of different aspects of animal welfare in egg production.

Both interviews and focus groups showed that customers were buying organic eggs because they were seen as healthier and avoided chemicals (80%). Sixty-five percent purchased organic eggs to avoid genetically-modified materials, and a similar percentage because they considered that the eggs tasted better. Seventy percent of respondents considered the chickens were in more humane conditions and were allowed to roam freely outside. Organic and free-range egg consumers were keen to avoid battery eggs, seeing these as 'egg-producing machines' with many chickens kept in close confinement, indoors, with artificial lighting possibly resulting in 'psychological disturbance'. In the case of free-range eggs, many respondents felt that they were unlikely to be getting a very genuine 'free-range' product. Organic free-range eggs were seen as being produced with organic feed and avoiding veterinary medicines. Improved bird welfare, in terms of housing and access to range were assumed to be adequately met in both organic and free-range systems. Organic units were perceived to be run to a high standard.

CONCLUSIONS

Consumer acceptance of organic poultry products depends on the nature of the production system. The extent to which poultry production standards vary is a cause for concern. Equivalence between organic poultry standards is essential for stable growth throughout Europe. It would appear that consumers expect a land-based production system, most effectively based around mobile housing with a smaller flock size. This would allow the poultry enterprise to be effectively integrated into the whole farm system, would ensure that pasture is adequately rotated and rested and would help to ensure that the birds effectively use the outside range area.

REFERENCE

EU (1999). *Council Regulation (EC) No. 1804/1999*, 19 July 1999. OJ L222, 24 August 1999.

ACKNOWLEDGEMENTS

Thanks to Sainsbury's Supermarkets Ltd for funding this work through the SOuRCe Organic Standards Group.